CHARLES VAN RIPER, editor   *Foundations of Speech Pathology Series*

Prentice-Hall Foundations of Speech Pathology Series

PRENTICE-HALL INTERNATIONAL, INC., *London*
PRENTICE-HALL OF AUSTRALIA, PTY., LTD., *Sydney*
PRENTICE-HALL OF CANADA, LTD., *Toronto*
PRENTICE-HALL OF INDIA (PRIVATE) LTD., *New Delhi*
PRENTICE-HALL OF JAPAN, INC., *Tokyo*

Foreign Accent

FRED M. CHREIST

Director, Speech and Hearing Clinic
University of New Mexico

Prentice-Hall, Inc., *Englewood Cliffs, N.J.*

editor's note

THE SET OF VOLUMES WHICH CONSTITUTES THE *Foundations of Speech Pathology Series* is designed to serve as the nucleus of a professional library, both for students of speech pathology and audiology and for the practicing clinician. Each individual text in the series is written by an author whose authority has long been recognized in his field. Each author has done his utmost to provide the basic information concerning the speech or hearing disorders covered in his book. Our new profession needs new tools, good ones, to be used not once but many times. The flood of new information already upon us requires organization if it is to be assimilated and if it is to help us solve the many different professional problems which beset us. This series provides that essential organization.

One of the unifying and outstanding features of all the volumes in this series is the use of search items. In addition to providing the core of information concerning his subject, each author has indicated clearly other sources having significance for the topic being discussed. The reader is urged to explore, to search, and to discover—and the trails are charted. In so rapidly changing a profession as ours, we cannot afford to remain content with what we have been taught. We must learn to continue learning.

Although each individual volume in this series is complete unto itself, the instructor should welcome the opportunity presented by the *Foundations of Speech Pathology Series* to combine several volumes to form the basic structure of the course he teaches. They may also be used as collateral readings. These short but comprehensive books give the instructor a thoroughly flexible teaching tool. But the primary aim of the authors of these texts has been the creation of a basic library for all of our students and professional workers. In this series we have sought to provide a common fund of knowledge to help unify and serve our new profession.

v

preface

MAN HAS OFTEN BEEN FORCED TO LEARN THE LANGUAGE OF HIS NEIGHBOR across the mountain or on the other side of the river. Commercial interests, clan needs, and the pleasure of social contacts frequently demand that he learn a new language. When the language is finally learned, he will doubtless find that he has a foreign accent. In this text, foreign accent will be considered the auditory results produced by the influence of native language patterns on those of a second language.

The behavior which we tend to diagnose and label as foreign accent is the occurrence of unaccustomed sound patterns in the speech of the second-language learner. Behind this behavior is a complex of cultural, linguistic, and psychological factors with which the speech pathologist and audiologist must be familiar if they are to serve the second-language learner in the clinic, the school, or the rehabilitation program.

That foreign accent has been significant to speech pathology and audiology since its earliest period is witnessed by Quintillian's admonition urging that a boy be taught Greek before Latin and insisting that the period of speaking Greek should not be too long. He reasoned that, "Such a course gives rise to many faults of language and accent; the latter tends to acquire a foreign intonation, while the former, through force of habit, becomes impregnated with Greek idioms, which persist with extreme obstinacy even when we are speaking another tongue...." (*17*)

The respect with which the American Speech and Hearing Association has always regarded this facet of speech correction is indicated by the fact that one of the earliest studies reported in the *Journal of Speech Disorders* was "Correcting the Mechanism Causing Most Foreign Brogue," by James L. Barker. Although the scope of ASHA has expanded with the passing years, the study of language differences, as indicated by resulting speech patterns, has not decreased. As in each of the special fields of clinical practice and audiology, other academic and professional specialists have expressed an interest. Some have even suggested that the subject, foreign accent, might be more thoroughly treated within their specialty. Foreign accent remains a rehabilitation area in which the specialist in speech, English, or language will need information. It will continue to be a clinical problem wherever two languages are spoken. The speech therapist is often the only person who can help.

With the continued influx of foreign students, laborers, and professional people into the United States, the demand for assistance will increase. Students contemplating the teaching of English as a second language in the expanding number of programs throughout the world today will require training in the problems of oral production and audition which their students will encounter. This book is written in an effort to introduce the student clinician and the speech correctionist to a portion of the extensive literature in the field of foreign accent.

Special thanks are due to G. Paul Moore, in whose *Symposium in Experimental Phonetics* an interest in foreign accent was created; to Raymond Carhart, whose encouragement led to the scientific study of sound discrimination in bilingual individuals; and to Charles Van Riper, who taught the author how to write a book. All that is valuable in the book is due to the stimulation of these teachers; all the weaknesses I claim as my own.

F.M.C.

contents

chapter VI

chapter VII

introduction

MAN TALKS AND AS HE TALKS HE HOPES TO COMMUNICATE WITH HIS fellow men. Wherever he lives, man talks with people. The hermit is out of time, at least he is out of style.

When man seeks to interest or inform, to entertain, to stimulate or to persuade his associates, the principal tool is speech. Patterns of speech will vary. Sound patterns of intonation or melody, silence in patterns of pause, designs of force in stress or emphasis, and meaning woven throughout—these will differ from one language to another. Always present is the desire to communicate, to influence behavior. Whether the speaker uses himself or another as his audience, it is part of the communication cycle, a cycle that gyrates within us and between us as humans.

 communication: in a first and second language

The ultimate end may be to influence for pleasure, for knowledge, or for action. Our talker may be seeking to express emotional frustration or joy in accomplishment. Whatever his purpose, man talks, and communication is his final objective.

Interference with the efficiency of communication may appear as man talks. Defects or insufficiencies of anatomical structure, deviations or damage to the neurological system, or functional aberrations of a normal human mechanism may affect the speech or hearing of the talker. When such problems appear, the speech pathologist or audiologist is called upon to assist in the habilitation of the speaker. Other books of this series present complete discussions of problems related to anatomical, neurological, or functionally disordered communication which will be encountered in the medical clinic, the school situation or the rehabilitation center.

FOREIGN ACCENT AND COMMUNICATION

Foreign accent introduces a peculiar problem into the area of speech pathology and audiology. Closely akin to functional articulation disorders but having many cultural implications, speech problems originating in second-language learning always appear in a bilingual or multilingual community. Second-language learning requires a change in patterns of intonation, stress, rhythm, and meaning in addition to changes in the distinctive sound units we call phonemes. Thus, the person with a so-called foreign accent can be said to possess deviations in articulation, rhythm, voice, and symbolization. These language patterns are habituated reactions which have been acquired in an intimate cultural setting and their replacement will not be easy.

Not only will the individual who brings his foreign accent to the clinic need special evaluation techniques and a clinician experienced in second-language therapy; he will also need high motivation. Although the individual with a foreign accent will appear in the speech clinic or the classroom requesting assistance, all authorities are not agreed that foreign students learning a second language should be handled in the clinical setting. Fully equipped and staffed

> 1a   Stevens, Bronstein, and Wong (64:285-86) reporting results of a survey conducted by the Speech for Foreign and Bilingual Student Interest Group of the Speech Association of America state, "We are aware, as are all other members of our interest group, that 'maximum exposure' to English is the best way to proceed. This procedure should encourage moving away from 'treating' persons with foreignisms as though such speakers all possess defects of speech." Where do these authors feel that English as a second language should be taught? And why?

institutes for foreign students are ideal but their prevalence at the present or in the very near future is limited. The client seeking new language patterns for communication will continue to overwhelm the school correctionist and apply to the speech pathologist in the clinic for assistance.

In the event a client appears with some variety of organic, neurological, or functional disorder and simultaneously exhibits a foreign accent, the problems are compounded. Examples of such double clinical entities found in the literature are the cleft-palate bilingual child and the bilingual stutterer.

> 2a   What is the relationship existing between bilingualism and certain speech defects? Johnson (37), Klinger (42), and Stewart (65) discuss the speech problems in relation to cultural backgrounds and language.

If you have ever attempted to administer a speech reception or auditory discrimination test to a native speaker of French, Italian, or Spanish or to evaluate an adult aphasic patient whose native language was Russian or Chinese, you can appreciate the complexity of speech problems for the bilingual. As a clinician, you will need both information and clinical practicum with foreign accent. Some day you may be the only help such a person can find.

A native speaker learns his speech "at his mother's knee" or at his father's, depending on the prevalent culture patterns of the society into which he is born. His language grows as he grows. Speech is not a mechanical process, a product of tonal patterns and articulations, but the very essence of man's nature and being. All he is or all he hopes to be is expressed in his speech. The Bible, the great tales of literature, poetry of every language, even many of the great theories of science were spoken before they were written. As the child matures, his language becomes more intimately a part of his life, his work and his recreation. Such deeply established habits become obstructions to new speech patterns demanded by second-language learning.

Having learned a native language and made it a part of himself, any individual may conceivably be forced to move into a new linguistic community. It is there that his communication problem will appear. If this person is young, flexibility permits the rapid adjustment to new habits of behavior and patterns of language change come easily. Adulthood increases the difficulty in learning a new speech pattern. The habits of youth have become the routines of age and replacement requires high motivation.

As transportation methods improve, the world becomes more intimate. Crises in our cold war society are constantly thrusting people of one language background into a strange language community. Communication becomes primitive as gesture language substitutes for oral communication until new habits can be formulated. As auditory perception improves, the newcomer begins to understand the new speech configuration. Motor speech habits are more slowly acquired. The speaker of a native dialect who attempts to learn English as a second language senses a conflict of language patterns.

FOREIGN ACCENT—A SPEECH DEFECT

Seated opposite you in the office is a native speaker of Spanish. He is seeking help, and as he talks American English in an effort to communicate his needs to you, a clinician who knows little Spanish, the discongruity becomes evident. The stream of speech is not that to which you are accustomed when a native speaker of American English is talking. Intonation moves in unaccustomed directions and the total melody has dissonances. Pauses are missing or misplaced and precise articulation of vowels and consonants which circumscribe the pauses are unfamiliar to an ear oriented to the soft glides of American English articulation. The staccato rhythm of your visitor's speech betrays a use of regular stressed and unstressed syllables. Certain sounds also are misplaced and distorted; the schwa sound, for instance, often precedes the initial sound of *s* in many words. As an interested listener and a pathologist, you wonder: Why can't I hear through his accent?

Your guest senses this breakdown in communication. He knows that he is not "coming through." Gesticulation may be added to his speech in an effort to make himself understood. Clinical questions become more measured in presentation. As you ask the questions, the added emphasis distorts the natural tempo of conversation to which you are accustomed with one who understands and speaks the dialect of the area. A shake of the head signals that your listener still does not understand.

A new start is made as you hope to remedy the situation, but you succeed only in adding emotional tension to the already disintegrating communication situation. This time the question is asked, "How long have you been in the United States?" Now the response comes easily for the question is a familiar one. Tension is relieved but further questions demand more intricate answers and the situation disintegrates once more.

Finally, your visitor, struggling to answer a question regarding his present work, flushes, looks about the room in confusion, mutters an unrecognized exclamation in Spanish and exits in frustration. After having rescued him as he rushes down the hall, you call for Theresa Marcus, a clinician who has just arrived. The interview can begin anew and communication will be more efficient, for Miss Marcus, being a true bilingual, speaks both Spanish and American English fluently.

All the elements of defective speech have been exhibited in this situation. *First,* the speech of the native speaker of Spanish called attention to itself. The same might have been true if the speech pathologist with whom he was talking attempted to converse in Spanish. *Second,* there was evident interference with the communi-

cation process. Exchange of ideas in either direction was impeded
by the inability of both participants to understand what was being
communicated. *Finally,* the evident frustration of the visitor, as well
as his rapid exit from the office, indicated, for the moment at least,
a temporary maladjustment. These features of the oral communication situation signify defective speech as defined by Van Riper
(*69*:16). "Speech is defective when it deviates so far from the speech
of other people that it calls attention to itself, interferes with communication or causes its possessor to be maladjusted." Since speech
as communication is to provide the basis for our discusion of foreign
accent, a definition of communication is needed as a point of de-
parture.

COMMUNICATION DEFINED

Communication has been defined in a variety of ways by individual research workers and authors. The meaningfulness of these definitions is dependent upon the knowledge of the field possessed by
the reader in which the discussion is being conducted and the purpose of the author. General definitions of communication in relation
to second-language learning are to be found in the literature. Webster defines communication as "intercourse by words, letters, or

> 3a   Have you ever developed a secret language? Did you use your high
>   school or college Spanish, French, German or Russian for communication
>   purposes? Berlo (*7*) and Miller (*50*) review aspects of the communication
>   system in relation to speech. Hall (*30*) relates the "silent language" to
>   cultural problems.

messages; interchange of thoughts or opinions . . . act, power or
means of communicating or passing from place to place." Such a
definition generalizes on the communication act in humans but
does not apply to communication systems within the animal king-
dom.

Cherry, a British researcher and scholar, has this to say. "Communicating is not the response itself but essentially the relationship
set up by the transmission of stimuli and the evocation of responses.
. . . it will be well to expand somewhat upon the notion of a stimulus; we shall need to distinguish between human language and the
communicative signs of animals, between languages, codes, and
logical sign systems, at least." (*19*) The problems of human communication discussed by Cherry as he elaborates on this definition
of communication are necessary background for any clinician in-

tending to work with foreign accent problems. The individual with a foreign accent is anxious to communicate. His response is essential in the communication cycle, but handling the basic process by which this response is patterned becomes the real problem.

Features of Language Design

The most thorough discussion of communication characteristics present in human and subhuman species has been developed by Hockett (*33*). Thirteen of the design features included in Chart I have been selected from his most recent publication relating to communication, both human and animal. These features have been discussed in more detail in the main body of the text.

CHART I

DESIGN FEATURES: FIRST AND SECOND LANGUAGE
AS REVEALED IN SOUND AND NON-VERBAL COMMUNICATION

Property	Human 2nd Language	Human 1st Language	Gibbon Calls	Meadow Lark	Bee Dance
*Interference	+				
†Tradition	+	+	?	?	probably not
Discreteness	+	+	+	?	no
Duality	+	+	no	+	no
Arbitrariness	+	+	+	+ if semantic	no
Vocal-auditory	+	+	+	+	no
Total Feedback	+	+	+	+	?
Specialization	+	+	+	+	?
Rapid Fading	+	+	+	+	?
Interchange-ability	+	+	+	?	+ limited
Displacement	+	+	no	?	+
Productivity	+	+	no	one or both	+
Semanticity	+	+	+	? partly	+
Broadcast	+	+	+	+	+

* Interference is a feature of languages in contact. Weinreich (*73*).
† Items No. 2 through No. 14 are described by Hockett (*33*) and Eisenson *et al.* (*26*)
The symbol + in the chart represents the fact that the characteristic is present in the communication system of the life form.

4a   Eisenson et al (26:141-59) relates Hockett's hypotheses to the psychology of communication. What would happen if a new-born meadowlark were taught the song of a thrush by controlled electronic recording or by direct association? Would he mature with an "accent," the song of the thrush, or his native song? Welty (74) presents a challenging discussion of this problem.

Interference

Second language learning introduces a feature of audition and production of sound symbols not discussed in relation to native language learning but essential to learning theory and speech pathology. When a previously learned habit is to be replaced certain events occur which facilitate or retard the learning of the new activity. Psychologists speak of "inappropriate response transfer," "habit interference," and "negative transfer" in relation to this situation. Either useful or useless influence may be transferred from the previous habit patterns. In second-language learning, the fact that some auditory and motor habits in producing sounds or sound combinations are useful while others interfere with new learning makes the problem more complex.

Forgetting, relearning, and overlearning are terms found in the literature relative to verbal conditioning and language. They are intimately related to all types of speech problems but, at present, of pertinence to the interference which occurs in second language acquisition. *Proactive inhibition,* the learning of one habit which interferes with the learning of a subsequent habit, is present in the foreign language situation. Listening to the speech of the person learning English as a second language, we often hear intrusions from their earlier language in the form of sounds, word forms, and structural arrangement of ideas. *Retroactive inhibition,* the forgetting of the original habit because of a subsequently learned habit, also contributes to interference by forcing forgetting of the first habit as a result of a habit pattern acquired at a later date. Some of your clients will no doubt accuse you of making them forget their native language in their attempt to learn English.

Evidence of interference between native language sound patterns, homophonous words, syntactical arrangement, and new speech habits will be recognized in the speech of the student. Detailed analysis of types and characteristics of each variety of interference to which the speaker is subjected will inform the clinician how to provide assistance in learning the language. Such interference reduces communication efficiency and, therefore, is the target of our attack on foreign accent.

Communication for Foreign Accent Defined

Since speech is a form of communication which makes the human animal superior to the other animal organisms, it is essential that we define communication in terms appropriate to this discussion. *Communication is a process for transferring materials, information, and ideas from a producer or source to a receiver or destination, utilizing a communication chain or medium.* The elements of this definition need explanation in terms of our approach.

First, communication is a process. The process approach to life has become more popular in the physical sciences, as well as in the social sciences. The anthropologist speaks of the evolutionary process, the analyst of a chemical process, a famous biologist refers to the "process of becoming."

> 5a   In developing his theory of morphogenesis, Sinnott (63) describes "creativeness" as a "process of becoming," the feature which differentiates living organisms from lifeless objects. He theorizes that within protoplasm there is a pattern which "so regulates the courses of the changes that go on within it that a specific form or activity tends to result." The process nature of communication is reflected in the writings of Berlo (7), Johnson (37), Mowrer (51; 52), and others.

Out of this new "process" perspective came the advances in modern communication science known as information theory and cybernetics. The process point of view underlies our concept of therapy for foreign accent. The constant changing of roles required in any speech communication system demands that the participant be speaker-producer at one instant and hearer-receiver at the next, or sometimes both at the same time. When attempting to juggle the elements in the communication situation and at the same time translate from the language heard to the native language and back into the second language, the process becomes submerged in the mechanics. You may have listened to a language of which you knew the fundamentals but in which you had little practice conversing. Soon you became lost in your attempts to translate a word not recognized automatically, only to discover when the job is completed that your listener was still waiting for an answer to a question you missed completely while struggling with the mechanics.

Second, communication recognizes transfer. Shifting of materials, information, or ideas in time relationships or space relationships becomes essential in this definition of communication. The process character of communication requires that these patterns of transfer are continuous as long as life exists.

Third, transfer implies that a producer and a receiver will be involved in any communication cycle. These individuals, in the case of the speaker with a foreign accent and the speech pathologist, may exchange places as the communication continues. When a receiver is included in the cycle, purpose is implied. Change of behavior is the purpose of the therapeutic regimen of the pathologist or teacher. Purpose, then, is an inherent part of the transfer facet of the definition.

Fourth, there are three entities—materials, information, and ideas —which can be transferred between producer and receiver in the process of communication. Materials, such as protoplasm, may be transferred in the creation of life forms as in the union of the spermatazoon and the ovary. In the human and certain mammals, biological communication of the male and female of the species permits the transfer of a male cell to the female uterine tube, where the fusion of cells takes place. Once growing, the organism must be provided with materials which foster growth and maturation. Food, oxygen, and minerals are provided through communication channels to satisfy the needs of a growing organism.

In any society there is need for transfer of materials to foster life and social well-being. Business thrives on the construction and sale of such materials. The second language learner frequently sees his need for reducing evidence of foreign accent in terms of accomplishment in this world of business. Thus, transfer of materials may take place either intra-personally or inter-personally.

The area of the world in which the creative process occurs will influence the native language spoken by your client. Most authorities agree that racial structural differences have no influence on the ability to produce selected sounds of any language.

> 6a   Interested therapists may desire to review the writing of Brosnahan (15)
> who does not agree. He suggests that it may be scientifically significant
> to reevaluate this generally accepted principle that all men have the
> same type of speaking apparatus.

Within the growing organism, the action of the nervous system represents the second type of transfer in the definition of communication, the transfer of *information.* Coded in a form which no one has yet been able to decipher, the nervous impulses travel along the nerve and across the synapses carrying information in afferent and efferent pathways to regulate the behavior of the receiver organism, as well as the producer. The client with a foreign accent will make use of his sensorium for receiving every type of stimulation which will assist him in adjusting to his problem. Each act will be directed by the information carried to the muscles from the cerebral cortex. Transfer of information becomes essential in the functioning communicator. (See Figure 2, page 5.)

In terms of our present knowledge, only man has *ideas* that can be transferred from himself to another for the purpose of changing behavior. Physical experiences are discontinuous. The symbolic nature of language makes possible the transfer of these experiences as ideas, thus making time binding possible. Ideas become a cohesive force in any language community. The clinician will be faced with the necessity of remolding ideas, for the second-language learner brings with him cultural ideas as a part of his native language.

An example of such a problem is the concept of giving in Navajo. Beals and Hoijer (5) describe the attempt to translate the English sentence, *I give it to him,* into Navajo, assuming that the word has the literal interpretation of presenting another with a gift. At first they found no word equivalent among the Navajo verbs which expressed the concept contained in the word *give.* After a search it was discovered that there are at least twelve forms in which the expression might be stated. After studying these various forms it was concluded that the Navajo concept of giving is spoken of as "object moving." They summarize their findings on the ideas of giving with the statement, "The act of giving, in other words, is differently conceived in the two speech communities, and the difference is codified in their styles of speech." Similar examples will be found in a variety of language communities throughout the world.

Transfer of materials, information, and ideas becomes a fundamental task of any communication system. In the operation of such a cycle, the efficiency of function will be dependent upon internal and external influences operating to facilitate or retard the basic objective of the system, the changing of behavior. The degree to which the communication system fails to accomplish perfect efficiency of operation is considered for our purposes the degree of "noise" in the system.

Noise

In this book, the term "linguistic noise" is used to indicate the reduction in efficiency of the communication process caused by language competition or overlap. The student should realize that this is not the use of the term in lay conversation where noise refers to "unwanted sound" nor is it the highly technical use of the term as in statistical communication theory. *Noise*, as used here, is a generic

> 7a   For the interested student, the technical approach to the word "noise" is contained in Shannon (62) and Cherry (19). A simple introduction to the idea of noise as a determinant in fidelity of communication is presented in Berlo (7). In addition a Symposium on Information Theory, presented at the 1951 Annual Convention of ASHA, Chicago, Illinois, is reviewed in the *Journal of Speech and Hearing Disorders*, XVII (June, 1962), No. 2, 166-97.

term and may be applied in such other forms as physical noise, psychological noise, semantic noise, physiological noise, and neurological noise. In each of the stated relationships the term *noise* will refer to *the reduction of efficiency in communication* created by the factor mentioned.

Thus, physical noise refers to interference created in the transmitting system by competing physical sound waves. Native speakers and speakers of a second language are subjected to such interference in equal amounts. Psychological noise is the reduction in efficiency created by the psychological state of the producer or receiver. This condition is experienced by the foreign student who fears speaking situations because of his feelings of insecurity in using American English speech. When damage to the neurological system of the body or physiological activities are reduced through disease or damage, the state of communication efficiency may be said to be determined by the neurological or physiological noise in the cycle of communication. A Chinese research assistant in the Chemistry Department who has a sensorineural hearing loss will experience a double problem in learning to speak English. His language problem will be compounded by his hearing difficulty, leading to the reduction in efficiency through two sources of noise, the linguistic component and the neurological component. Among the cleft-palate children seen at the Rehabilitation Center, Inc., during the last year were eight native speakers of Spanish and four Indian children of two different language groups. The difficulty which the clinician must face in doing speech correction work with these twelve children is a combination of linguistic noise and physiological noise.

These varieties of noise are found in the patterns of clients seen in the office of the speech pathologist or audiologist. Semantic noise, so frequently suspected in the communication breakdown of the stutterer, is that type of reduced efficiency associated with words, their meaning, or level of abstraction.

Linguistic noise is the problem of foreign accent. It is peculiar to human communication. When man talks, his efficiency is frequently reduced by the interference of one language background on a subsequently learned language configuration. In speech, such interference results in the production of foreign accent. Noise is always the clinician's problem; linguistic noise is the problem of the second-language learner and his instructor.

EXACTLY WHERE AND WHEN MAN BEGAN TO SPEAK REMAINS UNRECORDED. The sound waves of that first conversation are long lost. Unlike the wood of the primeval forests, they could not be petrified.

We can only assume that in some unique setting some primitive near-ape grunted or cried or yelped symbolically and was understood. Tools and fire were doubtless employed long before the dawn of speech, but it was only with the birth of the language symbol that "time binding" became a reality. Soon after this momentous beginning, in terms of cultural time, a father could tell his offspring how to skin and prepare his killed or captured food instead of demonstrating. Culture could be transferred by the spoken word.

B   *man, his speech and language as communication*

HUMAN LANGUAGE FOUNDATIONS

The New Testament says, "In the beginning was the word...." That first word might never have been uttered had the speaker been able to foresee man's future entanglements in the webs and wars of words. Yet, knowing also the creative genius that was born with the word, we can be thankful that it was spoken in the dialectal language of mankind rather than the reptile.

Charles Darwin said, "Man in the rudest state in which he now exists is the most dominant animal that has ever appeared on this earth.... Through his powers of intellect, articulate language has been evolved, and on this his wonderful advancement has mainly depended." (22) Once man had language, the entire pattern of his life was changed.

Having discovered the magic of symbolic utterance, man decided one word was not enough. Just as Adam and Eve could not be satisfied in begetting and raising Cain, so man, unsatiated with that first single "word," sought another and another. When that first meaningful word was uttered, the exigency of a second, a third and a fourth became apparent. With a reacting fellow human to understand and respond, verbal communication was born.

> **1b** How did speech originate? Would such origins influence the ability of man to learn several languages? Such questions invite a speculative answer because no objective evidence is accessible. This does not deter philosophers, psychologists, and anthropologists, as well as speech specialists, from theorizing. Gray and Wise (29), Hockett (32) and Brain (13) summarize the theories of speech development.

From our biological heritage comes the foundation for articulate language, whether native or acquired, as a second form of communication. These foundations are clearly animal in origin. Compare the heart, liver, lungs, or stomach of the human with those of lower animals and you will see little apparent difference. Study the reproduction or respiratory function and the reactions of muscle, nerve, and endocrine system at their lower levels and you will find the same systems operating in the higher animals and *homo sapiens*. The valving operation of the larynx has been adapted to new uses. The human being is "quite a new sort of phenomenon in the world. This difference, when analyzed, turns not on anatomy and physiology, but on behavior and accomplishment," according to Bates. (4) Man has the capacity to learn one, two, or many languages; the most highly developed anthropoid is incapable of learning even one.

Communication, Language, and Speech

Communication has been established as a "process." In Figure 10 is illustrated the relationships existing between speech and language in the process of communication. The process concept implies a constantly *changing* relationship between the producer and the receiver in any communicative situation. The speaker of a foreign language meets difficulty in such a situation because communication demands continuous flexibility in hearing and interpreting, as well as in arranging and producing his second language. This shifting position from being producer in one instant to being receiver the next compounds his difficulty. Consequently, this process feature of communication makes his adjustment to the speaking situation an added burden in learning a second language.

Language is a social phenomenon. The reader may choose to accept the "Divine Origin" theory or any one of the "evolutionary" or "accidental" theories for the beginning of speech. Regardless of the theory accepted by the reader, he will recognize that as a social phenomenon, speech has a structure and form which evolved as language was used in a particular culture. It is language that ties together the community of individuals who communicate in order to survive. For this purpose a systematic and often unexpressed set of rules for the use of words and the arrangement of these words evolves in every language. Language gives the *pattern* to communication through speech, and language is the product of the social factors in any culture. The second language learner will readjust his social habits as he moves from one language background to a second.

When patterns of social behavior differ between cultures, they will usually be expressed in variable ways through the speech of *the people*. Having learned the concepts of one cultural group and the speech forms associated with those concepts, the second-language learner moves into a new sociocultural environment where he may find his native habits of social usage inadequate. He must learn new speech patterns and, *with* these new sounds and noises, he will also learn the cultural patterns upon which the language is structured.

> 2b   Speech is said to unify human behavior. Whorf (77) provides a theory of the "ways of analyzing and reporting experience" as it influences language. Fletcher (27) finds speech a unifying factor in motor behavior for children but a possible deterrent for adults.

Some authorities define a language as a system of arbitrary vocal symbols by means of which human beings communicate and cooperate with one another. To others language is a form of symbolization which includes not only the vocal symbols which are a part of a speech communication system but the visible movements used by a speaker or the written words contained in a letter, magazine, or book. You, as a clinician, must decide what attitude you are going to take toward the definition of language. In the body of this text *language* has been considered *that body of traditional rules, symbols, and methods of expressing ideas for purposes of communication which are transferred culturally from one generation to another.*

Thus, sound patterns and gesture-symbols represent the overt evidence of the underlying condition for the speech pathologist or audiologist. John B. Newman expresses the concept for the therapist working with clients having a foreign accent when he says, ". . . it can be said that one does not *speak* language; for language, in this sense, is also an abstract construct, and one can *speak* only concrete actualities. What one speaks in this regard is that concrete actuality called dialect. Dialectal speech acts do constitute language, but only on an abstract level. Obviously, one does not speak communication: for communication is the impalpable process or force that generates and maintains the palpable, social, interactive behavior manifested as speech." (55)

It is speech that provides the vehicle for foreign accent. In speech we find the concrete, recordable evidence in which the problems of the second language learner can be studied and understood. As man talks, he uses sounds in a variety of ways. Moreover, these sounds are supported and amplified by certain symbolic gestures. Which element of the speech process came first is of no immediate concern for us here. Though patterns of movement and gesture are characteristic of various social groups and the language of signs and finger spelling are an intimate part of one philosophy of teaching the deaf, our present interest lies with the acoustic aspects of speech. Gesture language deals with the visible code. We deal with the audible.

> **3b**   The Italians and the French are frequently accused of speaking with their hands more effectively than with their tongues. Is this true? What would a Hawaiian dancer do without the language of the hands and the hips? Reusch and Kees (60) have studied the problem of nonverbal communication in relation to maladjustment. Birdwhistell (9) has suggested a science of gesture called "kinesics."

If we conclude that the relationship of communication, language, and speech is a process, an abstract construct, and a "palpable" objectively measurable feature of the underlying communicative process, we are prepared to analyze the speech of the individual.

Let us listen to a brief conversation heard this morning at the Student Union Building on campus. Jim Espanosa, leaving the building intent on a class in the College of Engineering, meets Jerry Caton, late for class but hoping to strengthen his morale with a cup of coffee before the class convenes.

"Hello, Jerry," Jim says as he opens the door for Jerry to dash through.
"Hi, how are things?" comes the reply.
"OK. Same with you?"
"Same," Jerry tosses over his shoulder as he dashes for the lunch counter.

What are the elements of speech found in this snatch of familiar conversation which might create a problem for any student of English as a second language? What principles of language are herein illustrated?

Language Is Conventionalized

If Jim or Jerry were to say the same words in a conversation on a campus of a foreign university, they might not be understood even by someone who knows English. In this social milieu, on this particular campus, among these conversing students, the words in this entire conversation have become conventionalized. Speech could not be communicative until a receiver of the symbols perceived the sounds, interpreted intonation and language patterns, and associated the result with previous experience.

When the stranger from across the mountain enters the community and speaks with a different set of conventionalized symbols, he is called a "foreigner" and his speech is frequently dubbed a "foreign accent." It is not solely the speech sounds which are deviate. The entire configuration of his language is different and calls the attention of the listener to the speaker's way of talking rather than to what he says. When we break the conventions of the language in any way and communication becomes impaired or difficult, the speech sounds defective. The problem may be severe enough to cause the speaker to become maladjusted. Many speakers with a foreign accent feel very insecure, even inferior. The minority complex in a bilingual society is a serious one, sociologically and personally. If we defy the conventions of language—however unconsciously or innocently—we may evoke penalty and frustration, mockery and rejection.

4b   To enjoy a delightful example of replaced conventions in English, read
     The Education of Hyman Kaplan (59).

Speech Sounds Are Arbitrary

When Jim and Jerry produced the conversation that morning at the entrance to the Student Union, the words exchanged were selected from past experience with the language. The sounds they used were arbitrarily selected from a battery of acceptable sounds and patterns of arrangement. Jim might have said, "I'm fine, thank you," instead of "OK," or he might have said "Je suis très bien, merci." If we study the first and last optional statement as recorded speech, there is evidence that the individual sounds selected for each language are familiar to the native American ear but the pattern of arrangement in word units is unfamiliar unless we have heard

French spoken. Yet, each of these patterns state the same general idea. Each language has a set of arbitrarily selected sounds, patterns and arrangements which have developed in the course of its historic development. Because of the arbitrariness of sound selection, the second-language learner frequently has difficulty in producing the new sounds of a strange language. For example, a glottal stop is difficult for American speakers to produce as an isolated noise or phoneme but certain Indian languages use the glottal stop consistently in word and sentence patterns. Babies use it frequently. In the same class is the tonal variation used as an indicator of meaning in certain African or Oriental languages. To the ear of the nonspeaker of the language, the speech pattern sounds strangely unfamiliar and we wonder why a people should choose to express important ideas in such an awkward arbitrary way. Speech sounds are arbitrary.

Language Is Systematic

In spite of the arbitrariness of speech sounds and word combinations, the fact that language has system makes work with foreign accent possible. Though the speaker may seemingly interject the language system of his native language randomly into the second language, it is possible to study his production and to show that his mistakes are not random at all. The work of linguists provides valuable information for the therapist working with foreign accent. As

> **5b** Linguistics is the *science of language*. Speech is language according to the approach in this text. Bloomfield (10) is the "grand old man" of linguistics. Gray and Wise (29) have a chapter on the "linguistic basis of speech." Joos (38) introduced acoustic analysis into phonemics.

one's knowledge of the English language and its structure, as well as its phonology and semantic characteristics, increases, the systematic comparison of the native language of our client and the second language he is attempting to learn will make it possible to understand his sound substitutions, distortions, omissions, and additions. Because language has system, it is possible to plot the patterns of that system and to study those parts of the pattern carried over into the second language.

When Jim and Jerry meet other friends in other situations, they will make other statements. Each statement and response will be structured, in terms of verbal symbols, in a systematic way familiar to the speaker of American English. The listener may understand the statement, in spite of his inability to analyze the system of the language, but full meaning of a strange language can only come when the systematic arrangement of symbols is understood automatically and immediately.

These three characteristics of language will be met by the speech pathologist in his work with foreign accent: the characteristic sounds and sound patterns in speech, the conventional aspects of both the native and the second language, and the systematic character of both languages. If we are willing to accept the work of structural linguists and the descriptive linguists, we may find our job of working with foreign accent becomes not only more objective but more rewarding.

AMERICAN ENGLISH, THE SECOND LANGUAGE

When an individual chooses English as his second language he learns a particular dialect. If he chooses American English as his dialect he will have narrowed his selection to one variety of English. In making this choice he hopes to learn to "talk American," to communicate in American English speech. The ideolect our student chooses to speak will reflect the overlap and interference between his native tongue and his new speech.

The speaker comes to America or he remains at home to learn the new way of talking. He brings his family or he comes alone, intent on acquiring the advantage of a double culture. He could have chosen England, France, Africa, Russia, China, or one of a dozen other countries. Wherever he goes, he takes his native language with him and it invades the new tongue he seeks to master. He will have problems. New speech learning is inevitably tied to motor skills, habits, and cultural behavior. All speech is learned; the *sounds,* the *structure,* the means of expression must be acquired. Since speech has *meaning,* the student will need new associations to build new meanings for sounds and structure of the language he has selected.

Having chosen American English speech, the second-language learner assumes the burden of new habits, new modes of thinking, and new patterns of behavior. In speech is reflected not only the sounds and structures for communication in the society in which he has decided to live but also the story of its past and the projection of its future.

Similarities and Contrasts

The words, American English, in the title of this section, provide the starting point for our discussion of similarities and contrasts in speech. As a dialect of English, American English is not a single entity that can be described under the three divisions of sound, structure, and meaning. There are variations in each of these divisions of language to be discovered in the dialects of American English. Such variations are especially noticeable in phonology or sound production. Within the classification of American English is included all of the English spoken throughout North and South America, as well as the dialects of the Hawaiian Islands and Alaska. Such geographic diversity is matched by the speech diversity of the inhabitants living within those boundaries. Speech styles would include the "pidgin" and "polyglot"; the "General American" and the "Standard British." Therefore, General American speech must be defined more specifically for making comparisons with the native language of the student and the client to determine the degree of foreign accent present.

If we restrict our discussion of foreign accent to the consideration of a *single* dialect within the dialects available in the continental boundaries of the United States, we will meet differences of opinion regarding speech patterns.

> 6b Are the traditional classifications of southern, eastern, and general American dialects still tenable? Bronstein (14) illustrates the relationship existing between American English and all other branches of English in terms of pronunciation. Thomas (66) designates ten dialect areas. Wise (78) presents a detailed discussion of the major areas and their present subdivision.

The dialect selected by the second language learner will be an accident of location. The section of America to which he comes and the dialect area from which his teacher comes will determine the special speech pattern of English he will be taught.

The divisions of American English available for use in second language learning are outlined in Figure 6. English may be learned as a *primary* language; it is both native and primary in such countries as the United States and most of Canada. It may be learned as a secondary language (as an academic requirement of his education system), or it may be learned as an adjunct to the *native* language of the country because of the social, political, or economic advantages of speaking the tongue. In each of the last two instances,

English becomes the *secondary* language of the individual. This situation exists in some parts of Mexico, the countries of South America, the islands of the Caribbean, and, to some extent at present, in the Hawaiian Islands. In either primary or secondary use of American speech, there may be evidences of foreign accent. General American English will provide the basis for discussion of foreign accent when English is learned as a secondary or "target" language.

Speech as Language

We must face the problem that in speaking of language we are using a term which implies a variety of concepts. For the linguist, language is speech, and all other forms of representation, such as writing or gesture symbols, are secondary means of communication, related to, but not essentially being, the essence of language. For the speech pathologist and the audiologist, the term "language problem" cannot be restricted to the speech symbols. Although speech is the "palpable reality," it is a symptom of other conditions which exist in the language system of the individual. Language will be used to apply to the *structure* as illustrated in Figure 5. The terms "inner language," "written language," and "gesture language" will be used to refer to various other manifestations of the structure in the process of communication.

Related areas of experimental investigation and teaching contribute to the study of speech as language. For purposes of identifying sounds and their characteristics, and for facility in the notation system adopted, in the following chapters we will be using terms from a number of specialties. From linguistics the terms phone, phoneme, allophone, and morpheme are adopted. Since they may be new terms to some readers, the following definitions will apply in the use of the terms.

Phone: A phone is a speech sound that is a member of a phoneme.
Phoneme: A minimum unit of distinctive sound feature.
Allophone: Any variation in phonetic production of a phone which makes up a phoneme.
Morpheme: A sequence of phonemes which has meaning and is not composed of smaller units having meaning.

> **7b**   Are these new terms to you? If you have not heard them in your anthropology class or linguistics class, you may find them in Lado (*44*), Trager and Smith (*67*) and Hockett (*32*).

RECEPTION AND PRODUCTION OF SPEECH

Man *hears* sound and makes sound. He *listens* for significance in the sound patterns which he hears. When the individual *associates* these sounds with meaning and understands, he is involved in communication and may be ready to make an oral response. In this three-stage process, the foundations of speech are laid. In our sound-filled world, these foundations are inseparable from the development of speech in the normal individual.

The Reception of Speech Sound

Satisfactory hearing provides the groundwork for first- or second-language learning. Studies of the deaf and hard of hearing demonstrate a decrease or absence of speech responses following the early stages of babbling. A human hearing mechanism, neurologically and physiologically intact, makes language learning easier. Those children handicapped in hearing, listening, and associating meanings must acquire language by using sensory avenues other than audition. Acquired by generalization and discrimination, language develops progressively from birth. Indeed, certain authorities have delineated stages of sound discrimination development similar to those designated for the acquisition of speech. Modern teachers of English as a

8b   How did you learn to hear the sounds of speech? Carhart (18) outlines the stages of development in sound discrimination. Beebe (6) indicates stages of auditory memory span correlated with chronological age but "not consistently with each change in age" level.

second language have recognized the importance of the *hearing, discriminating, associating* cycle in language learning and have developed the so-called aural-oral method as one of the most effective systems of training.

Can you tell the difference between a "loud" and a "soft" tone? Many foreign students cannot recognize such differences in gross sound. Have you ever tried to teach rising inflection or falling inflection patterns to a student who did not recognize pitch change? Hearing gross rhythm patterns or "beat" in speech or music is difficult for some American students as well as for those learning English as a second language. If you find this difficult to believe, watch some of the dancers on the ballroom floor or listen in on a poetry class some day. Such gross features of American English speech must be heard and reproduced before they can be used in the subtle ways that tone, pitch, and rhythm are used in speech.

Every language also has its "distinctive" speech sounds, as well as its meaningful melody patterns. These sounds and sound patterns

> 9b Perhaps you have been confused by the use of the term "phonetic" and "phonemic" found in the literature on phonetics and foreign accent. Bloomfield (*10*), one of the early authorities on descriptive linguistics, defines a phoneme as "a minimum unit of distinctive sound features." Kantner and West (*39*) explain the two terms for speech pathologists and audiologists. Joos (*38*) explains the contrasting terms from the linguistic point of view. Hultzen (*34*) contrasts the two views.

have significance for the person who knows the code.

Soon it becomes necessary to establish discriminative responses to varying elements of the speech pattern on the basis of gross sound recognition as used in the second language. An example may illustrate this concept. Certain Spanish students have difficulty in differentiating auditorially between the sound of [ɪ] in "tin" and the [i] in "teen" when heard in conversation. This discrimination appears essential for them only in the learning of American English since in Spanish the two sounds are only variations of the same phoneme. The native Spanish speaker seldom needs to listen to differences between the [i] and the [ɪ] sounds in Spanish. To understand a speaker of Spanish one never needs to discriminate between these two sounds. To understand an American speaker of English does require the making of this type of fine discrimination. This ability to hear fine differences between related sounds in a language is developed early in life and is the second important step in sound evaluation for the purpose of learning a first or second language.

Finally, the ability to make sound discriminations under adverse listening conditions also appears to be important. Such discriminations must be made when "noise" is present, either as an outside interference, defined as "physical noise" in our discussion of communication, or as an internal interference. By internal interference we refer to the linguistic, semantic, psychological, physiological, or neurological "noise" presented in Introduction A. The second-language learner is forced to make sound discriminations under adverse listening conditions; the native listener has learned to conquer them during his early language development. In their native languages, most children have learned by the age of three to make the necessary auditory discriminations even under unsatisfactory listening conditions.

Reception comes first in the process of speech acquisition and the ability to differentiate significant from insignificant sound elements of any language must be learned by children before they can talk. If the adult is to acquire the same facility or even a minimal facility in speaking a second language, he must begin by *listening, discriminating, associating, and by recognizing distinctive sound patterns of the speech* of that other language.

Production of Speech

A review of the research indicates that the earliest age of appearance of the first word is 9-10 months and the latest age is 18-19 months for children of normal physical and mental capabilities. Before this event has occurred, the child has passed through a series of stages or periods of maturation in sound production. Reflex production of sounds, beginning with the birth gasp or cry, continues during the "pre-lingual" stage of development. As the motor efficiency of the articulatory mechanism improves and the neuromotor skills of the infant progress, babbling of random sounds and the production of self-entertaining noises can be perceived in the sound repertory of the infant.

> 10b Osborn (56) states the case for these contrasting philosophies of speech development. Mysak (54) presents the development from the attitude of the "holistically oriented clinician." The studies of Irwin and his associates (36) and Darley and Winitz (21) survey the literature on early sound acquisition and first words used. Van Riper (70) makes you laugh as you learn the principles of teaching your own child to talk.

Once the "fun" of speech production has been discovered, the "mewling and puking" infant is on the long road to the unavoidable semantic entanglements to which our generation is destined. He now begins to echo his admirers and imitators. The more they imitate his chained noises, the more he echoes their imitations until the seeming enthusiastic adult tires of the game and it is necessary that he go on making the sounds for his teddy bear or rattle. He now talks even to those confining sides of the crib which formerly he draped with stringed beads of sound. This period has been called the "echolalic" phase of speech development. Out of the generalizations of sound production emitted at this stage come the shaped sounds called words.

Then suddenly everything has a name: the objects you perceive, the things that you do, the way you feel. It becomes enjoyable to play with those words and with the people who make them. The child soon learns also to use those words to control his environment. As he begins to "talk," he uses conventionalized sound patterns to obtain appropriate responses from the people in his control area. "How they love to fetch and carry for me when I use the right word," our child concludes. So the pattern of sounds-responses, sounds-responses is repeated hundreds of times each day. The vocabulary of discriminative words is growing. It begins to bloom when the child discovers that two words can be put together, then three, then four. Now speech for communication is beginning to develop.

In primary language learning the process is rarely planned or controlled. If parents enjoy their children, they play with them, talking all the time and reacting to the sounds they make. If parents have unwanted children, they frequently isolate them physically and acoustically or fail to talk and play with them. Imitation is essential in the process of speech learning and the constant bombardment of the child with the sounds of language in a pleasurable setting makes language learning a source of *fun*. The process of early physical maturation with its absorption of all types of sensory stimuli is unimpeded by concern with other problems. When the child cries, he is fed, or changed, or entertained by fondling or with *talk*.

Contrast with this the learning of a second language for communication. There are constantly conflicting demands made on the child or adult who is anxious to learn a new speech pattern.

First, the speaker begins with a highly developed sound repertory from his native language. These established sound patterns often conflict with the new sounds he is attempting to learn. The learner has not had the freedom of the child to sample a wide variety of sounds and then to select those which are most usable after playing with many patterns.

Second, the nature of reinforcement for the learner is different in first- and second-language learning. While the child receives immediate response to his demands and oral stimulation is constantly present, the student of a new speech pattern must seek out stimulation of the type needed in the second language. His friends are often busy speaking their native tongue. The sound environment offers conflict rather than reinforcement as it impinges on his ears.

Third, in certain settings the friends of the second-language learner may ridicule him for attempting to learn a new speech pattern. While the parents and friends of the child learning his native language encourage each attempt to make sounds, words, and phrases for communicative use, the friends and relatives of the second-language learner may laugh at his attempt or castigate him for desiring to move outside the cultural sphere of the native language, thus adding negative reinforcement.

Fourth, the baby has no choice when learning his native language; his discrimination patterns are set by the sound environment in which he finds himself. The second-language learner, on the other hand, must constantly make choices between the native and the second language in *sounds, structure,* and *meaning.* He must also choose between two languages when economic, social, and professional welfare are at stake. The child has not yet reached this stage of decision.

Fifth, the second-language learner is frequently taught by the method of building up a collection of sounds and vocabulary words, one at a time. This contrasts with the method of first-language learning in which the patterns of speech are selected from a broad collection of reflex and randomly produced sounds. Attempting to learn individual sounds and words and spending most of the time on those sounds with which he has most difficulty often causes a loss of the over-all configuration of speech for communication. At the same time the *fun* of the process is lost; it may become *drudgery* for the second-language learner. Although teachers and clinicians are utilizing the "patterned" practice method of learning a second language, it is never possible to obtain the same patterned flexibility present in learning a first language.

When man begins to speak, he listens first and makes sounds as he listens. When response comes to these sounds the symbol words appear. Each language has its individual set of symbols in sound and word. The child learns language as a pleasurable experience in the association with his parents and friends as they respond to his mouthings. He selects the sounds for use in any language from the broad repertory of sounds he has practiced producing. When the situation demands that the child or the adult learn a second language, difficulties arise. Linguistic and psychological noise develops in the communication system of the speaker. First-language learning and second-language learning are not the same process and various language backgrounds will give different forms of foreign accent. A thousand languages in the world today could produce a thousand varieties of accent. ᘐᘐᘐ

bibliography

1. Allport, F. H., *Social Psychology* (Boston: Houghton Mifflin Company, 1924).
2. Anshen, Ruth N., ed., *Language: An Enquiry Into Its Meaning and Function* (New York: Harper & Row, Publishers, 1957).
3. Barker, James L., "Correcting the Mechanism Causing Most Foreign Brogue," *Journal of Speech Disorders,* I (1936), No. 1, 3-12.
4. Bates, Marston, *Man in Nature* (Englewood Cliffs, N.J.: Prentice-Hall, Inc., 1961).
5. Beals, Ralph L., and Harry Hoijer, *An Introduction to Anthropology* (New York: The Macmillan Company, 1959).
6. Beebe, H. H., "Auditory Memory Span for Meaningless Syllables," *Journal of Speech Disorders,* IX (1944), 273-75.
7. Berlo, David K., *The Process of Communication* (New York: Holt, Rinehart & Winston, Inc., 1960).
8. Berry, Mildred, and Jon Eisenson, *Speech Disorders, Principles of Therapy* (New York: Appleton-Century-Crofts, 1956).
9. Birdwhistell, Ray L., *Introduction to Kinesics* (Washington, D.C.: Department of State Foreign Service Institute, 1952).
10. Bloomfield, Leonard, *Language* (New York: Holt, Rinehart & Winston, Inc., 1933).
11. Boas, Franz, *General Anthropology* (War Department Educational Manual) (Boston: D. C. Heath & Company, 1938), pp. 124-45.
12. Braidwood, Robert J., *Prehistoric Man,* 5th Ed. (Chicago: Chicago Natural History Museum, 1961).
13. Brain, Lord, *Speech Disorders: Aphasia, Apraxia and Agnosia* (London: Butterworth & Co., Ltd., 1961).
14. Bronstein, Arthur J., *The Pronunciation of American English* (New York: Appleton-Century-Crofts, 1960).

15. Brosnahan, L. F., *The Sounds of Language: An Inquiry into the Role of Genetic Factors in the Development of Sound Systems* (Cambridge: W. Heffer and Sons, Ltd., 1961).
16. Buhler, Karlotta, *The Mental Development of the Child* (London: Routledge & Kegan Paul, Ltd., 1930).
17. Butler, H. E., *The Institutio Oratoria of Quintillian*, 4 vols. (London: Cambridge University Press; William Heinemann, Limited, both 1953).
18. Carhart, Raymond, "Auditory Training," in *Hearing and Deafness*, Rev. Ed., Hallowell Davis, ed. (New York: Holt, Rinehart & Winston, Inc., 1960), pp. 368-86.
19. Cherry, Colin, *On Human Communication* (Cambridge, Mass.: The Technology Press of the Massachusetts Institute of Technology; New York: John Wiley & Sons, Inc., both 1959).
20. Clark, W. P., *The Indian Sign Language* (Philadelphia: L. R. Hammersley & Company, 1885).
21. Darley, Frederic L., and Harris Winitz, "Age of First Word: Review of Research," *Journal of Speech and Hearing Disorders* (August, 1961), pp. 272-90.
22. Darwin, Charles, "Descent of Man," in *The Origin of Species and the Descent of Man* (New York: Random House, n.d.).
23. Davis, Hallowell, Gordon E. Peterson, and Warren Weaver, "Information Theory," *Journal of Speech and Hearing Disorders*, XVII (June, 1952), 166-97.
24. De Fleur, Melvin L., and Otto L. Larsen, *The Flow of Information* (New York: Harper & Row, Publishers, 1958).
25. Dunn, Halbert L., "Communication and Purpose—Ingredients for Longevity," *Journal of Speech and Hearing Disorders*, XXVI (May, 1961), 109-17.
26. Eisenson, Jon, J. Jeffery Auer, and John V. Irwin, *The Psychology of Communication* (New York: Appleton-Century-Crofts, 1963), pp. 141-59.
27. Fletcher, Samuel G., "Speech as an Element in Organization of a Motor Response," *Journal of Speech and Hearing Research* (September, 1962), pp. 292-99.
28. Forum, *ASHA*, V (April, 1963), 616.
29. Gray, Giles Wilkeson, and Claude M. Wise, *The Bases of Speech*, 3rd Ed. (New York: Harper & Row, Publishers, 1959).
30. Hall, Edward, *The Silent Language* (Garden City, N.Y.: Doubleday & Company, Inc., 1959).
31. Hibben, Frank, *The Lost Americans* (New York: The Crowell-Collier Publishing Co., 1961).
32. Hockett, Charles, *A Course in Modern Linguistics* (New York: The Macmillan Company, 1958).
33. ———, "Logical Considerations in the Study of Animal Communication," in *Animal Sounds and Communication*, W. E. Lanyon and W. N. Tavolga, eds. (Washington, D.C.: Publication No. 7, American Institute of Biological Sciences, 1960), pp. 392-427.
34. Hultzen, Lee S., "Phonetics, Phonemes and Teachers of Speech," *Quarterly Journal of Speech* (April, 1949), pp. 202-6.

35. Irwin, Orvis, "Infant Speech: Effect of Systematic Reading of Stories," *Journal of Speech and Hearing Research,* III (June, 1960), 187-90.

36. ———, and Han Piao Chen, "Infant Speech: Vowel and Consonant Frequency," *Journal of Speech and Hearing Disorders,* XI (June, 1946), 123-25.

37. Johnson, Wendell, *People in Quandaries* (New York: Harper & Row, Publishers, 1949).

38. Joos, Martin, *Acoustic Phonetics* (Baltimore: Waverly Press, 1948), Language Monograph 23.

39. Kantner, Claude, and Robert West, *Phonetics,* Rev. Ed. (New York: Harper & Row, Publishers, 1960).

40. Kellog, W. N., and L. A. Kellog, *The Apes and the Child* (New York: McGraw-Hill Book Company, 1953).

41. Kenyon, John S., and Thomas A. Knott, *A Pronouncing Dictionary of American English* (Springfield, Mass.: G. & C. Merriam Company, 1944).

42. Klinger, Herbert, "Imitated English Cleft Palate Speech in a Normal Spanish Speaking Child," *Journal of Speech and Hearing Disorders,* XXVII (November, 1962), 379-81.

43. Kohler, W., *The Mentality of Apes* (New York: Harcourt, Brace & World, Inc., 1925).

44. Lado, Robert, *Linguistics Across Cultures: Applied Linguistics for Language Teachers* (Ann Arbor: University of Michigan Press, 1957).

45. Langdon-Davies, John, *On the Nature of Man* (New York: New American Library of World Literature, Inc., 1961).

46. Lemert, Edwin M., "Some Indians Who Stutter," *Journal of Speech and Hearing Disorders,* XVIII (June, 1953), No. 2, 168-74.

47. Leutenegger, Ralph R., *The Sounds of American English: An Introduction to Phonetics* (Chicago: Scott, Foresman & Company, 1963).

48. Lewis, M. M., *Infant Speech* (London: Routledge & Kegan Paul, Ltd., 1936).

49. Mallery, G., "Sign Language Among North American Indians," First Annual Report of the Bureau of Ethnology, Smithsonian Institution, I (1881), 279-80.

50. Miller, George A., *Language and Communication* (New York: Mc-Graw-Hill Book Company, 1951).

51. Mowrer, O. Hobart, "Hearing and Speaking: An Analysis of Language Learning," *Journal of Speech and Hearing Disorders,* XXIII (May, 1958), 143-52.

52. ———, "Speech Development in the Young Child," *Journal of Speech and Hearing Disorders,* XVII (September, 1952), 263-68.

53. ———, "The Psychologist Looks at Language," *American Psychologist,* IX (1954), 660-92.

54. Mysak, Edward D., "Organismic Development of Oral Language," *Journal of Speech and Hearing Disorders,* XXVI (November, 1961), No. 4, 377-84.

55. Newman, John B., "The Categorization of Disorders of Speech, Language and Communication," *Journal of Speech and Hearing Disorders,* XXVII (August, 1962), No. 3, 287-89.

56. Osborn, Suzanne Smith, "Concepts of Speech Development," *Journal of Speech and Hearing Disorders*, XXVI (November, 1961), No. 4, 390-92.
57. Piaget, Jean, *The Language and Thought of the Child* (New York: Meridian Books, Inc., 1959).
58. Prator, Clifford, *Manual of American English Pronunciation*, Rev. Ed. (New York: Holt, Rinehart & Winston, Inc., 1957).
59. Rosten, Leo, *The Education of Hyman Kaplan* (New York: Harcourt, Brace & World, Inc., 1937).
60. Ruesch, Jurgen, and Weldon Kees, *Nonverbal Communication* (Berkeley: University of California Press, 1956).
61. St. Onge, Keith, "Articology," *ASHA*, V (January, 1963), 499.
62. Shannon, Claude, and Warren Weaver, *The Mathematical Theory of Communication* (Urbana: University of Illinois Press, 1949).
63. Sinnott, Edward W., *Matter, Mind and Man* (London: G. Allen & Unwin, 1958).
64. Stevens, Cy, Arthur J. Bronstein, and Helene H. Wong, "English as a Second Language—Practices of Speech Departments," *Quarterly Journal of Speech*, XLVIII (October, 1962), No. 3, 285-96.
65. Stewart, Joseph, *The Problem of Stuttering in Certain North American Indian Societies*, Monograph Supplement No. 6, *Journal of Speech and Hearing Disorders* (April, 1960).
66. Thomas, Charles K., *An Introduction to the Phonetics of American English*, Rev. Ed. (New York: The Ronald Press, 1958), pp. 191-215.
67. Trager, George L., and Henry Lee Smith, Jr., *An Outline of English Structure*, Studies in Linguistics, Occasional Papers, No. 3 (Norman, Okla.: Battenburg Press, 1951).
68. Travis, Lee E., Wendell Johnson, and Jayne Shover, "The Relation of Bilingualism to Stuttering," *Journal of Speech Disorders*, II (1937), 185.
69. Van Riper, Charles, *Speech Correction: Principles and Methods*, 4th Ed. (Englewood Cliffs, N.J.: Prentice-Hall, Inc., 1963).
70. ———, *Teaching Your Child to Talk* (New York: Harper & Row, Publishers, 1950).
71. ———, and Dorothy Edna Smith, *An Introduction to General American Phonetics*, 2nd Ed. (New York: Harper & Row, Publishers, 1962).
72. *Webster's New Collegiate Dictionary* (Springfield, Mass.: G. & C. Merriam Company).
73. Weinreich, Uriel, *Languages in Contact: Findings and Problems* (New York: The Linguistic Circle of New York, 1953).
74. Welty, Joel Carl, *The Life of Birds* (Philadelphia: W. B. Saunders Co., 1962), pp. 204-8.
75. Whatmough, Joshua, *Language, A Modern Synthesis* (New York: The New American Book Library, 1960).
76. Whitney, Elwood, ed., *Symbology: The Use of Visual Symbols in Visual Communication* (New York: Hastings House, Publishers, Inc., 1960).
77. Whorf, B. L., "The Relation of Habitual Thought and Behavior to Language," *Language, Culture, and Personality*, Leslie Spier, *et al.*,

eds. (Menasha, Wis.: Sapir Memorial Publication Fund, 1941), pp. 75-93.

78. Wise, Claude M., *Applied Phonetics* (Englewood Cliffs, N.J.: Prentice-Hall, Inc., 1957).

79. Yerkes, R. M., *Chimpanzee: A Laboratory Colony* (New Haven, Conn.: Yale University Press, 1943).

80. Young, Robert W., *The Navajo Languages* (Mimeographed edition prepared for the Appendix of the 1960-61 Navajo Yearbook).

THE SOUNDS OF AT LEAST TWENTY-FIVE HUNDRED LANGUAGES CAN BE heard in the world today. But the majority of the world's population speaks only a "native" language, and there are many within those populations who cannot read or write what they speak. Indeed, some languages of the world have no system for writing the sounds produced in speech. Linguists are engaged in recording and analyzing some of these unwritten languages before they become "lost tongues."

Most men, born into a given society, learn one language, and only one, for communication. In those countries where residential requirements, political expediency, or commercial necessity demand

1 *speaking one language and more*

that the resident learn a second language there is an effort to become proficient in another tongue.

BILINGUALS

There are areas in the world where members of the population learn to communicate in two or more tongues. In certain countries, such as Switzerland, Belgium, Holland, Luxemburg, and the independent states of Africa, the ability to speak a number of languages fluently is a requirement for social existence. In the New World many countries speak two or more languages, but according to Fogelquist (*41*:23-27), only one, Paraguay, is truly bilingual. Such an atmosphere fosters foreign accents of all varieties, as the world traveler can well appreciate.

The word *bilingual* usually refers to a person who has the ability to speak two languages. The true bilingual has such command of both languages that he is able to converse in either language, as the occasion demands, and can "think" in either language without translating. Such persons are relatively rare. Many unusually talented individuals acquire the ability to speak two languages and switch from one to the other at will, but the majority of bilinguals, so-called in the literature, have "accents" in one of the two languages.

POLYGLOTS

Reference will be made to the *polyglot* as a person who has "a confusion of languages." The speech symptom of the polyglot condition will be of major significance to the clinician.

Juan Romero says, "I *e*study my lesson," yet he was born in the Southwest and has spoken English all of his life. Juan reveals other symptoms of the polyglot condition as well as the addition of the schwa sound [ə] before the *s* of the word *study*. This condition can be explained on the basis of his double-language background. A carefully prepared analysis of his total speech pattern would probably reveal that a similar schwa addition appears frequently when *s* is used initially in other words.

The polyglot condition that exists in the United States today is comparable to a similar speech condition found in other countries of the world. In such cities as Hong Kong, Paris, Tokyo, and London, the fusion of populations from many cultures leads to the establishment of native language islands within the limits of each city. A similar situation exists in such American cities as New York,

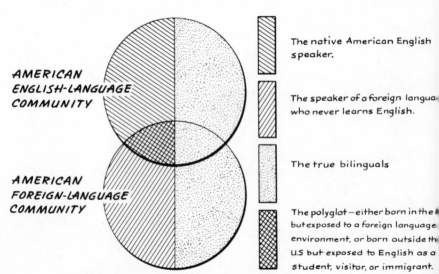

Figure 1. Monolingual, Bilingual, Polyglot.

Chicago, New Orleans, San Francisco, and Los Angeles, as well as in several states. Louisiana, Minnesota, Pennsylvania, and parts of the Southwest and West have large percentages of their populations representing one or more foreign-language groups.

Frequently, these groups isolate themselves completely. Even though they are surrounded by English-speaking neighbors, some groups attempt to preserve their language and customs to the exclusion of the American ways and the use of American English. They fight a losing battle, of course, and their children suffer. If the parents maintain their original language and insist upon speaking only that language in the home, their children often adopt a "creolized" type of American English, which is fostered by the attitude assumed. The schools of these linguistically diverse communities contain children at all levels whose speech reflects the influence of prejudice against the language of the country adopted.

> 1 You may ask: What attitude shall I take toward bilingualism in the community in which I am serving as a teacher, speech therapist, or clinician? Haugen (58:87-118) reviews attitudes and suggests approaches for the bilingual individual in society.

Examples of such attitudes are seen in the Indian grandfather who says to his grandson, "Go, learn the talk and ways of the white man. But when you return to the reservation, you will speak the language of the people and live as they live, forgetting the white man's talk." Similarly, the father of a recently arrived Middle European family says to his daughter, "No, you cannot attend the public school until you have taken your first communion in the native language of your parents." Reactions such as these create psychological noise for the second-language student. His feeling of confusion, in addition to the conflict between his "native" environment and his school and work environment, affects his language behavior.

In contrast to the situation in which the foreign community refuses to accept the language of the new country and reflects this attitude in the individual homes of the community, a second condition of nonacceptance sometimes arises. The language of the parents is *not* regarded as "the only acceptable language for this house" by the child; instead, it is a social stigma from which he must escape. When the atmosphere of taboo is fostered by social surroundings, the reaction on the part of the child is often one of revolt. He may reject everything connected with the language and the culture that fosters it. An understanding attitude on the part of the instructor

2   Such statements as these are frequently heard in the classroom or the
    clinic: "The Angelos act stuck up to us because we don't dress so good
    or talk the same. We feel they're out to get us." "I'm a Hunky because
    I talk different." "They won't hire me because I talk like a Jap." These
    problems and attitudes are discussed by Haugen (58:395-406) and Wein-
    reich (147).

or clinician becomes an important part of the polyglot's adjustment
to the speech situation. Social status is often determined as much
by the speech one uses as it is by the color of the skin, the way one
dresses, the job one holds, or the number of cars in the driveway.
Psychological noise disturbs the symbolic function for which language provides a structure. The attitude which accompanies a speech
"inferiority" is as real as the segregation that accompanies the
prejudice.

You have all experienced some minor difficulty in understanding
the speech of an American from the southern or eastern American
dialect district if you speak General American English. Kurath and
his associates are in the process of subdividing these dialect areas
into small patterns of variation for the future dialect geography of
the United States. (83) We need not be fearful of losing our clients
with a foreign accent. With or without an international language,
institutes of English, school systems, and speech clinics will be over-
whelmed with requests for assistance in learning to speak American
English "without an accent."

SPEECH LEARNING—SECOND LANGUAGE LEARNING

The word *learning* appears prominently in all discussions or writ-
ings on foreign accent. Since it is generally agreed that language is
learned and not transmitted genetically, a review of the methods
of teaching language is important for the therapist. Miller (104)
implies that it is as difficult for psychologists to agree on learning
as it is for a group of theologians to agree on sin. Authorities have
attempted to explain verbal learning for the first or the second language on the basis of Pavlovian conditioning, the Law of Effect,
imitation, cybernetics, Gestalt psychology, Field Theory, and the
autistic theory, to suggest only a few approaches. Verbal behavior is
a complex art involving variables in the producing situation and
in the listening situation, operating in the same subject simultaneously. The speaker is the listener and the patterns of action are
determined by the "feedback" taking place during the speaking act
as well as during the listening phase of the cycle. Experiments in

delayed feedback have emphasized the significance of these variables on the verbal behavior of the individual.

> **3** Why is it that no psychological theory of learning is sufficient to explain all the factors in verbal learning? Krasner (82) offers the most up-to-date review of the conditioning theories of verbal learning. Mowrer (109) has maintained a prominent place in the theory of learning applied to language development.

Many psychological theories are used to explain the process of learning a first or second language, but two principal methods of teaching language have been prevalent in modern educational literature: the *direct method* and the *structural method*.

The direct method, eulogistically referred to as the *natural*

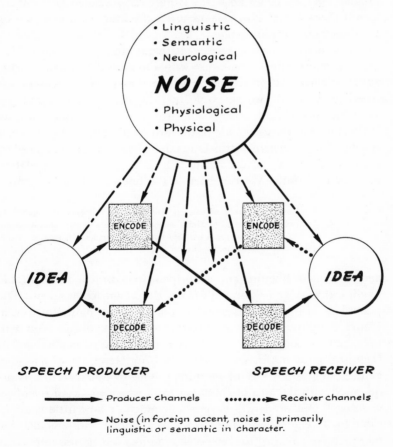

Figure 2. Foreign Accent in the Speech Communication System.

method or the *mother's milk method,* attempts to use principles discovered in studying the development of speech in the child. It also
assumes that children have been learning a second language easily
and have been speaking that language fluently since the spoken word
was evolved. "Languages are learned, not taught," contend the advocates of the natural method. The most effective setting for such
learning is the "natural setting" in which the child practices sound
combinations, structural patterns, and meaningful expressions associated with familiar objects, situations, and ideas. Because this
methodology was successful with young children, it was tried with
pre-adolescents, adolescents, and adults. At adult levels of maturation the method proves to be less successful, because it lacks challenge
for the older speaker who needs more clearly defined goals. Much
speech therapy with language-impaired children has been based on
the direct-method philosophy.

The structural method receives its name from the structural linguists whose findings, combined with those of the descriptive linguists, provide the principles on which the system is founded. As
speech pathologists, we can profit by using the precise information
available in the field of linguistics for work with foreign accent.
Writers who advocate the use of the structural method outline their
system of approach in intricate detail. The clinician will need to
study the principles of the system if he is to use it as a foundation
for speech therapy. We can borrow the findings of the structural

> 4   Should the speech pathologist and audiologist become a linguist? Al-
>   bright and Albright (1:51-55) emphasize the role of linguistics in speech
>   and hearing therapy. Lado (86) outlines the method to be used in con-
>   trasting two language patterns.

and descriptive linguists and adapt principles which are applicable
to clinical work and classroom work with foreign-accent clients. The
phonology of linguistics is based on the phonetic analysis of speech.
Figure 3 indicates areas of investigation in linguistics. You will
note that the area called *semology* is one of the main divisions of
linguistic study outlined by Joos (73:53-70). He describes *semology*
as the "linguistic study of meaning." The speech specialist is ac-
quainted with the area of *semantics* from which the word *semology*
is derived. Our needs will govern how much or how little is applicable for foreign accent. The details of grammar and semology are
more remotely related to the speech symptom but no less important
in the total problem of foreign accent. Every language has its own

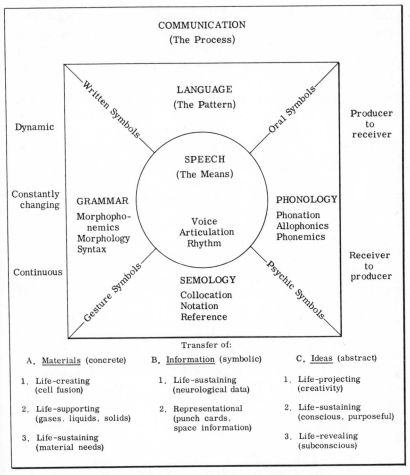

Figure 3. Communication, Language, and Speech. The frame of reference for English from the linguistic point of view is an abridgment of George Trager's outline (139).

grammar, determined by the culture plus historic changes in the development of that culture.

The word *grammar* has two general interpretations. *First,* the traditional meaning of grammar refers to a body of rules and regulations applicable to the use of verbal symbols or written symbols in communication. These rules were maintained on the assumption that they were logical and consistent. Consequently, they provided the structure for any language to which they were applied. *Second,* the *new grammar,* as it was called when first introduced, differs radically from traditional grammar in its concept of structure. This approach bases the grammar structure of any language on the *use* of the rules by a speaker of the language. Advocates of this philosophy of grammar apparently work under the assumption that rules which are not generally observed in language usage are not rules but dogmatic pronouncements, established by some self-styled authority in the discipline.

> 5   If you have been harassed by the seeming discrepancy between rules and practices in spoken and written English, you will enjoy a visit with H*Y*M*A*N* K*A*P*L*A*N and the puzzles of English speech and grammar as presented by Rosten (122).

Grammatical structure does deal with the things people say, and for that reason, it is of importance to the speech specialist; but it is more than a "practical" science to the structural and descriptive linguist. Just as the first division of language study delineated by the linguists is *phonology,* the second area of scientific investigation is *grammar.* By grammatical structure is meant the system of formal devices by which certain meanings and relationships are conveyed to the listener. Because of these "systematic formal devices" in any language, it is possible to compare the two languages and to define likenesses and differences in the structure existing between those compared. For the clinician, the approach of the new grammar offers an objective method for analyzing the needs of the student who consistently carries over the functional, as well as the structural, components of his native grammar system into the newly acquired speech.

> 6   The linguist divides grammar into three classes (see Figure 3) for purposes of analyzing the details of structure and function. These parts are morphophonemics, morphology, and syntax. Should you desire to dig more deeply into such complicated subjects you will find them in Carroll (22) and Joos (73).

Language forms, functions, and syntax are as significant for the speech pathologist as they are for the linguist, but the application is pragmatic as well as theoretic. When the student moves from the sound patterns of his native language to the sound patterns of a second language, he becomes trapped in the maze of grammatic inflections, both structural and vocal, as he changes from one language to another. Statements of such items as person, number, gender, case, and intention are presented in different manners.

The child acquires these habits of structure in his native language before he has reached school age. His imitation of adults and his hearing and repeating of inflectional patterns of voice make the changing forms come easily. He never thinks or cares about the rules. Examples of errors by analogy which frequently creep into children's speech, such as *foots* for the plural *foot* and *gived* for the past tense of *give,* illustrate the maturing process of grammatical imitation.

The second-language learner cannot depend upon his ear as the child does. Time does not permit such a relaxed attitude toward the problem. For example, the native speaker of Spanish has difficulty with questions in English. In his native language he says, "Es un medico" (Is a doctor?); in his second language the statement is, "Is he a doctor?" Two problems will be noted by the clinician; the frequent omission of the pronoun in the speech of the student with a Spanish-language background and the varying intonational pattern to which the clinician may not be accustomed in General American Speech. These features become a basis for comparing the grammars of the two languages; contrasting elements are plotted and a general principle is established as valid for the language being investigated. Such information is invaluable for the speech clinician when he attempts to answer the question: Why does José repeatedly raise his voice at the end of a question to a pitch that seems to leave the question hanging in the air and incomplete? José does this and frequently omits the pronoun reference in the English statement of the question because they are grammar patterns intruding on his learning of English. The structural approach can assist the speech pathologist with such a problem as with other items of grammar in the language.

Teachers of foreign language espoused the findings of linguists in *phonology* and *grammar* and built "patterned practice" as a way of

7 We use "patterned practice" in the speech clinic, and, therefore, it should be available as a technique for the clinician who works with foreignisms. Finocchario (37) provides a program for using the method with children in a classroom situation. Rojas (121) prepared the Fries American English Series for use in the schools of Puerto Rico.

learning a second language. Based on the aural-oral philosophy of repetition through questions and responses in the particular pattern on which the instructor plans to work at the time assigned, the method is reputed to develop the verbal flow pattern of normal speech, while it builds the habits of sound production, word configuration, and native grammar inflections. Used in such countries as Puerto Rico, Mexico, the Philippine Islands, and the Latin American republics when first introduced, the method has since been introduced in Asiatic countries and Africa.

Patterned language learning has provided a basis for attacking problems of speech while utilizing the linguists' contributions in phonology and grammar. At the present time, the area of semology is somewhat less useful to the speech pathologist working with second-language problems. It is scarcely beyond the definition stage in linguistics.

> 8   Are *semology, collocation,* and *notation* strange words to you? Perhaps you will be discouraged when you fail to find them in a dictionary. If you need to look them up, you will save time by reading Joos (74:53-70) after having studied Trager (139:163-171).

For this reason the speech specialist should use the term *semantic* as it has been used in speech to explain the problem of second-language learning. Certainly, linguists will soon be able to provide the basis for analyzing semology in second-language learning to such an extent that we, the teachers of speech, will be able to utilize their findings in our work.

Semanticity is that characteristic of language in communication which depends upon the associative ties previously established between the producer, the receiver, and the objects or situations, both internal and external to the communication environment of the participants. Our interest is in the behavioral evidence of such semanticity.

A former student explains the importance of meaning and semantic implication to the Navajo:

> Some people who come to work with the Navajos—those who speak only one language—often do not realize the tremendous handicap in not being able to understand and speak English fluently. One time a Navajo driver was asked to back a large truck. His foreman shouted, "Back upa shade!" The driver didn't understand the meaning of the word *shade.* You can imagine how many misunderstandings and hazards result from the language problem. One man argued intensely over the word *resign.* He insisted that his daughter didn't resign—she *quit.* (He was probably confusing the word *resign* with *fired.*)
>
> Sometimes misunderstandings come when a Navajo doesn't realize the power—the connotation—of the English words he is using. He may have heard these words used and not realized that they are not acceptable for all times, places, and people. (A tape recording, *A Word in Your Ear,* explains the importance of this.) The person may be saying things which come out differently than he intended. This needs to be considered by the White listener.*

* Polacca, Kathryn, *Trial and Error—of Understanding,* from materials duplicated for use in the Workshop on Second-Language Teaching, New Mexico State Department of Education. 1962

The problem illustrated is made evident in the classroom where we frequently hear such expressions as, "She dozen no what she read," "You post to be in school," and "When we read we have seeds to sit." Such oral problems are transferred into writing in the attempt to express ideas in English. Each problem reflects the results of cultural influence and speech habits.

HABITS OF SPEECH AS LANGUAGE

Speech and writing, as well as other forms of communicative behavior, depend upon patterning for their usefulness. As demonstrated by the examples presented, inversions of words and substitution of sounds or letters, by accident or because of language background, can produce humorous or sometimes grotesque alterations in meaning.

Beginning with a few sounds, vowels or "vocoids," consonants, and diphthongs or "diaphones," man makes sound symbols to meet his needs. These symbols, when arranged in patterns and given significance by experience, form the matrix of speech. By adding variations in melody to these patterns, man makes it possible to change the function and meanings of the words so formed. In English, such words as 'record, the noun, and re'cord, the verb, illustrate the principle used in innumerable words in English. By changing the stress from the first to the second syllable, one changes the function of the word from a "name" to an "action" word; this, in turn, changes the meaning. In other languages of the world, changes in pitch or "tone" may serve to vary the function and meaning of a pattern of sound components grouped together as a word form.

More elaborate patterns of sound are required when words of a series are chained to express ideas. Arrangement of these patterns will make a difference in meaning. "Jack kicked the horse" and "The horse kicked Jack" both use the same four words, but the arrangement will make a difference. (Both Jack and the horse might be concerned about the order of the statement.) In the actual situation expressed by the spoken symbols, the resulting action will differ in proportion to what actually occurred. Thus, patterns of arrangement will effect the meaning.

An infinite variety of patterns for sound symbol arrangement are available in the vocal mechanism. Fortunately, each language has a finite number of speech patterns that can be analyzed and plotted in areas of sound, structure, and meaning. However, meaning has yet to be analyzed in sufficient detail for use in the clinic or classroom. We will be looking at the methods of analysis and their use in the following chapters.

Man is a creature of habit and his speech production reflects this nature. When patterns of native language have been learned, their use becomes automatic and unconscious. Among 127 million inhabitants of the earth, more than twenty-five hundred languages have become habituated. A speaker of any one of these languages finds it difficult or impossible to understand a speaker of another language because of the habit patterns he has developed. When this same man attempts to learn to speak a second language, the habits of the first create *interference.*

In summary, we have noted that twenty-five hundred or more languages have crowded the air waves of the world with "talk." *First,* with such a variety of ways available to express an idea, misunderstandings are certain to arise. An international language has been designated as one means of clarifying such misunderstandings and improving communication in the world. *Second,* some individuals have found it necessary, or at least desirable, to learn *more than one language.* When this person so integrates the languages learned that little or no foreign accent is evident, we consider him a true *bilingual.* The *polyglot,* in contrast, has been identified as that person who uses a "confusion of language" in such a way that it causes him to speak with a foreign accent in one or both of his languages. *Third,* languages differ in sound components, and these are studied as *phonology.* Every language has a *grammar* which is the structure that permits analysis. Inherent in each language is *meaning,* the present challenge to students of speech and language studied as *semology.* Since each language has an individual sound system, a characteristic grammar structure, and a meaning based on the culture, when two languages overlap, these patterns may interfere, creating *foreign accent. Finally,* most men learn only one language, but those who venture into learning a second will find difficulty when the languages compete and they will need assistance in speaking.

FIRST MAN LISTENS, THEN, HE INTERPRETS WHAT HE HEARS. FROM THE maze of sounds he selects those patterns that have meaning for his life. Out of the "noise," patterns emerge and man struggles to understand their meanings. Man began listening as he entered this world of unceasing sound. Having heard that first choked cry of birth, he cried and listened, babbled and listened, building the structure of his speech. Crying led to sounds of other types: the soothing sounds, the wondering sounds, the comforting sounds, all pleasant to the ear. Each sound prepared a way for another. The listening child experimented with the sounds he heard in life. Slowly came the sounds of speech, crudely formed at first, then pat-

2

speech and language interference

terned for response. Soon man controlled his life and the lives of others with the sounds he heard and made.

Into such a native-language environment, the sounds of a foreign tongue intrude. When man listens to foreign speech he hears new sound symbols, strange signs that do not fit his experience. The sounds are perceived, but the patterns are unfamiliar. No meaning is conveyed by them. Response breaks down because the intrusive symbols have no hooks in previous training, practice, or experience. Language interference has been introduced.

Language Overlap

The term *overlap* has been selected to describe the condition that exists when two or more languages are learned by the same person. Defined formally, overlap means "to extend over *and beyond*"; the "and beyond" represents the multidimensional character of language influence designated in Figure 4. Degrees of interference in language overlap will vary from zero, in the case of the true bi-

lingual or multilingual, to any percentage which makes the interference a factor in learning the second language. Theoretically, this
percentage could reach 100, at which time the interference would be
so complete that the subject would not be able to speak either
language. Clinically, this is an impossibility, because there are a
sufficient number of factors of similarity between languages to prevent a completely "alinguistic" individual from developing. The
literature does provide evidence that delayed speech frequently has
its sources in a bilingual conflict, but sufficient evidence is lacking

> 9   Have you worked with any children whose problem was "delayed
> speech"? Bilingualism is frequently mentioned as a cause of this condi-
> tion. Berry and Eisenson (7:110-11) relate bilingualism to retarded
> speech. Lambert and Fillenbaum (87:455-59) discuss the condition of
> aphasia among bilinguals.

to prove that the condition is solely related to the point-for-point
interference of one language with another.

A distinction has been established between the so-called *compound*
bilingual and the *coordinate* bilingual. The compound bilingual is
one who develops the same meaning for translated equivalents in
the two languages to which he is accustomed. In contrast, the coordinate bilingual maintains separate meanings for concepts, objects, or actions in either language. Each of these two conditions
will be influenced by interference.

Interference

The word *interference,* introduced in Figure 9, refers to the intrusion of one language upon another. Evidences of such intrusion
are heard as deviations of phonology, grammar, and meaning from
the norms of speech in either language. Such intrusions are considered the result of language overlap.

Any clinical investigation of interference should begin with audition. It is generally conceded that language is learned through
auditory generalization and discrimination, whether the language
is native or subsequently acquired. Certain polyglots will be found
who understand the second language when spoken by others but are
unable to produce the speech patterns in a way comprehensible to
a native speaker of the language. At the opposite extreme is the individual who has learned to speak the language with some degree
of fluency but has difficulty following the conversation conducted by
a group of native speakers, especially when they begin to use technical terms or humorous idiomatic references. The initial question in

our evaluation of foreign accent might be: How much auditory interference is present?

INTERFERENCE IN RECEPTION

Audition

We must begin our search for interference in the physical characteristics of sound and its reception by the human organism.

> 10   Since theories of sound reception and its relation to language develop-
>   ment are necessary to a statement of perception of language, you can
>   prepare yourself by reading in Davis (30:387-40) and the studies of
>   Hanley (53:1-10).

The *broadcast* characteristic of language as communication provides the basis for audition. Sound waves produced by the speaker
must be heard before they can be interpreted. The hearing ability
of the receiver may influence the ability of the listener to interpret
the sounds of any first or second language. Since language symbols
are broadcast, the first variables which will be considered as interference are factors outside the language itself.

Pure-tone audiometry and speech-reception testing, if it can be
accomplished without handicapping the individual because of his
language background, are evaluation requirements in any work with
foreign accent. One would hardly require Steven Horka, whose native language is Hungarian, to discriminate auditorially between
the [t] in *tread* and the [θ] in *thread* if he had a radical binaural
high-frequency loss. Methods of teaching this phoneme would need
to be varied in such a way as to take cognizance of his physiological
or neurological problem. *Hearing evaluation* becomes the first step
in preparing to face interference as a problem of second-language
learning.

Environmental control of the speech symbol includes provision
of a reasonably efficient sound isolated physical setting in which the
instruction is to be accomplished and where adequate speech
samples of the language being learned can be presented. Modern
"language laboratories" provide the technical equipment needed
for supplying a standardized sound stimulus and for recording the
results of such stimulation.

Three factors then will effect the speech stimulus received by the
student:

1. The hearing acuity of the subject.

2. Conditions of relative quiet or sound isolation of the room in which evaluation and instruction is to be conducted.

3. The method of supplying sound stimuli to be used for instruction.

Perception of Speech

The next major concern in audition is the ability of the individual student to make fine sound discriminations in a variety of sound patterns used in speech. It is here that PB lists prepared for

11   Lado (85:46-104) provides a useful outline for testing of the foreign-language student in perception and production of speech.

all major languages would be useful to the clinician assisting with foreign accent as well as to the audiologist testing for discrimination with or without a hearing aid.

Research in acoustics, linguistics, experimental psychology, and experimental phonetics has supplied keys to the puzzle of relating the physical characteristics of speech and perception of sound patterns. Studies made by audiologists and speech pathologists Lane and Moore (89:232-43), Stevens and House (134:111-28), and Winitz and Bellrose (152:171-80) are contributing to a better understanding of the mechanisms involved. The speech clinician should utilize such findings to improve the auditory perception of students with a foreign accent.

Among the factors influencing perception of speech signals that have been named in research reports are the following: verbal facility, kinesthetic conditioning or feedback, tonal detection, ability to synthesize, formant influence, position of sound in context, duration of sound, redundancy, resistance factors such as distortions and masking, sound spectra, vocal memory, and unpleasantness. With such a variety of elements active in the perceptual situation, it is easy to appreciate the complexity of perception as a part of the speech process. Only future research will give the final answer. At present, research workers are not ready to say to the clinician: Here are three, five, six, or even ten principles on which auditory perception is based in second-language learning. If you investigate your client's ability in the perception of English speech and bolster his ability where needed, you will lay a foundation for reducing his foreign accent.

We sometimes have the idea that research is something that demands elaborate equipment, advanced statistical know-how, written reports, and a fancy vocabulary. Every clinical problem should provide a stimulus for some type of research project.

12   Read Lado (85:44) for suggested experiments and study. Your assistance
     is needed in this field of foreign accent; so little is known about so
     many enigmatic questions.

We may generalize from the findings available at present by saying:

1.   Auditory perception of speech is related to the physical characteristics of the produced sound patterns.
2.   There appears to be a relationship between the kinesthetic result of producing the sound of a language and the perceptual result.
3.   Perception is related to the setting in which the patterns appear. The phonemes are influenced by the position and order of the pattern in which they appear. As therapists we need to teach perception of a given phoneme in those *positions:* initial, medial, or final at which these sounds regularly appear in American English. They should also be taught in *relation to* the various phonemes with which they usually appear.
4.   Resistance, "distortion, masking, or unpleasantness," in the form of linguistic or psychological noise, will affect the perception of sound patterns in a second language. Miller and Nicely (*106:*153-75) present examples of such interference within the consonants of English. The speaker of two languages does not make random errors in perceiving sounds of the new language; there is order and reason for these "mis-hearings."

Evaluating Perception

The clinician, having established the state of hearing acuity for the student, must evaluate his ability to make those finer discriminations necessary for speech. Principles for the construction of such tests have been discussed. Once the areas of need in training perception of sound patterns in American English are delineated, the instructor is ready to study the points of interference present in the perception of speech sound patterns of the second language.

When the monolingual learns his native language, he is faced with the problem of comparing every phoneme learned with every other in order to acquire the significance of "distinctive" difference between these sounds when forming meaningful units. Long before he reaches school age he learns by generalization and discrimination which sounds belong in certain positions within various speech patterns. The second-language learner must match each new phoneme with every other phoneme in his native language, as well as with every other phoneme in the new language, before he can be confident that he has the phoneme system of his second language under control. In terms of effort, irrespective of the learning mechanism involved, this process of auditory matching demands constant vigilance. The child acquires this ability automatically in his native language during the parental "bombardment" period and the interference is minimal. If he is exposed to a second language early enough, speech in that language also becomes spontaneous, because his habits of language have not become "set." *The adult tends to relate to his native sound system all the sounds he hears.* He must be taught methods for discriminating the difference which appears blurred at first hearing. He has difficulty because of his native-language listening habits.

As evidenced in Figure 5, the ideal bilingual would speak without language interference. His language overlap would be so organized that in his coordinate or compound system of language relationships he could produce the speech of either language at will. The phonological system, the grammar structure, and the semantic control of each language would be so integrated in the bilingual that no interference would be evident. This was illustrated in the diagrams. Language A parallels language B in all its features. Interference is absent though overlap is present and speech perception appears normal in either language.

Our polyglot, on the other hand, because of his confusion of tongues, finds it impossible to make the perceptual evaluations necessary to compartmentalize his languages. In learning to speak he has generalized from one language to the other and has never been taught to discriminate between the two sound systems, the structure of the grammars, or their semantic expressions.

When evaluating the ability of a second-language learner to perceive verbal patterns and meanings in the target language, we are obliged to test:

1. Phoneme recognition in the native and second language and the ability of the listener to distinguish between these features.
2. Recognition of sound features of stress, intonation, and time as they function in the two languages.
3. Ability to identify sound patterns related to the grammar system in both native and second language in order to discover points of interference.
4. Auditory recognition of meanings in structural patterns and in idiomatic expressions as they differ between the two languages.

INTERFERENCE IN PRODUCTION

Though hearing, listening, and perceiving are primary stages of language learning, production is at least half the process. The Indian, Charlie Waterflower, can laugh with the rest of the group if he fails to understand what is said. He can ask that the question he failed to understand be repeated, just as the native speakers do. However, when he tries to say, "He fell in the ditch," and says, "He fell in the dish," everyone will laugh and look at him. The part that hurts is that they will be laughing *at* him, not *with* him.

The Russian student who comes to the clinician with the statement, "I want to speak English as the Americans," should be alerted by a question related to the applicant's native language: "Have you ever heard an American who spoke your native Russian like a native?"

This will occasion some thought concerning the effort involved in learning to speak a second language like a native, and would open the way for discussion of the difficulties encountered in learning a second language as an adult. It should be pointed out to the applicant that the maximum result to be anticipated would be a form of speech which would not call attention to itself, nor cause interference with the communication being attempted, and would certainly not cause the speaker to become maladjusted.

It is hoped that as the result of such a discussion the student would achieve an objective, realistic attitude, enabling him to appreciate the problem involved and the work required to rid him of his "foreign accent."

SPEECH INTERFERENCE

Speech is the result of a motor act and every speech event is the product of some individual language background. The neurological and physiological function of a human organism produces the sound patterns of that event. When the native speaker listens to the speech produced as a second language, he evaluates the result primarily in terms of communicative effectiveness. If the listener is attracted more specifically by the sound differences in the way ideas are presented—whether these differences refer to phonological characteristics, grammatical and syntactical characteristics, or semantic characteristics—than he is to the ideas communicated, the speech is said to be defective. The speaker will be considered as one having a foreign accent.

> **13**   How do you recognize foreign accent and interference? Chaiklin (25: 165-70) explains the variability of listeners' evaluation of foreign dialect. Weinreich (147) defines interference and relates it to speech and language.

We will need to differentiate here between dialect, foreign dialect, and foreign accent on the basis of speech and language evidence. In reference to dialect, there are, according to most authorities, three primary dialect areas in the United States; the Eastern, the Southern, and the General American. Each of these dialects have speech differences evidenced in phonology, if not in other characteristics of language. Yet, we do not designate a speaker from one of the areas other than that in which we were raised as one speaking with a "foreign dialect." Most countries of the world have at least two comparable dialects within its language area. Often the dialectal influence extends well outside the boundaries of the country. You will hear the language teacher of the native Spanish student say, "He speaks Mexican Spanish," or "Those new arrivals use a Cuban dialect when they speak Spanish."

A *dialect* is defined on the basis of *idiolects* by the linguist. An idiolect is "the totality of speech habits of a single person at a given time." We will consider a dialect as a collection of idiolects that have speech characteristics in common. In the example presented above, when the student says "dialect," he is referring to the Spanish spoken in Mexico where each individual native Mexican is exhibiting an idiolect of the Mexican dialect as he speaks. Out of the stream of American English has developed the variety of English dialects spoken by natives of the United States and those of other countries in the Western Hemisphere as seen in Figure 4.

When we speak of a *foreign dialect* in referring to dialectal variations, we will be referring to a dialect of some language other than English. In this way it will be possible to differentiate "foreign dialect" from "foreign accent." The Cuban arrivals speak a foreign dialect when they speak Cuban Spanish, and students who do not speak Spanish may say, "He speaks a foreign dialect." These students who have learned their Spanish in the university language laboratory may have difficulty understanding what they are saying at times, but they could say, "Juan speaks a Mexican dialect."

Finally, we will reserve the term *foreign accent* for those polyglots

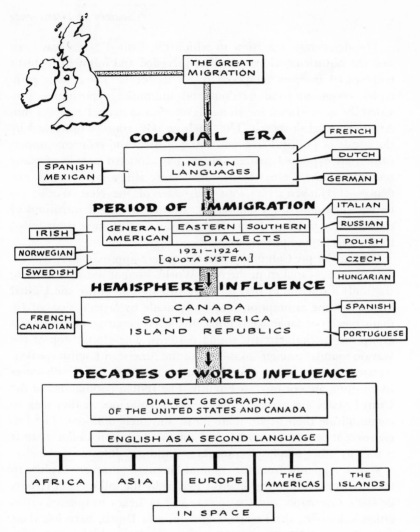

Figure 4. The Evolution of American English.

who have a speech and language overlap which leads to interference between the native language and their second language, American English. Foreign accent, for the clinician, is the symptom of the polyglot condition. It is the auditory evidence of his confusion of languages that may be heard as he speaks. Such acoustic results of his motor speech act and the behavior patterns on which they are founded make it possible for us to say he has a *foreign accent.*

Sources of Interference

The democratic tradition in which the United States was born and the historic developments that preceded and followed its birth emphasized freedom of speech in all its forms. These basic principles, communication freedom and unlimited opportunity, provided the groundwork for an amalgamation of many languages into American English speech. The "melting pot" concept buttressed by the ideals of political freedom, social justice, and economic opportunity, all expressed in free speech, has attracted people of many tongues. In the United States today there still remain speech evidences of Haugen's *(59)* four languages of the New World: *(a)* native, *(b)* colonial, *(c)* immigrant, and *(d)* creolized. Intrusions of each of these language forms on American English have contributed to the interference phenomenon.

During the pre-Columbian era there were approximately 350 Indian languages spoken in the New World. Present statistics indicate that only a fraction of that total are still spoken within the United States, but the assumption frequently made by laymen that all Indians speak one language is fallacious. Each language of the Indian group has its characteristic sound patterns. The glottal stop of the Navajo sounds "foreign" to the ear of the American English speaker. Tonal patterns used in some Indian languages to signal differences in meaning are not used in English. The Indian populations of the United States are becoming more speech conscious as they seek to communicate their needs, their ideas, and their opinions. The foreign-accent problem is no less real for the American Indian than it is for any other non-English-speaking child or adult.

Speech remnants from the colonial language group are evident in the Southwest, where the Spanish spoken by the followers of Cabeza de Baca, Coronado, and Onate may still be heard in isolated areas. Other colonizers, the French, Germans, and Dutch, have left their languages to live after them in parts of the United States. The speech influence of the early colonizers is often strengthened by attraction of immigrants speaking the same language to a common settlement area. Thus, the original Spanish influence on the United States has been strengthened by a constant stream of new arrivals during each decade, most recently the Puerto Rican and Cuban groups. Speech interference is perpetrated by an influx as each new group of immigrants brings revitalizing influence on the "mother" tongue.

Foreign accent has been most frequently observed among the immigrant group. During periods of political, social, or economic upheaval, the immigrant found his way to the United States. He may have been forced to depart or he may have left his homeland by choice. In either instance, these speakers of another language came to us, bringing with them their native speech. From Ireland and parts of the British Empire; from every part of Europe, northern, southern, and western; from the Americas; from the islands of the Pacific; from the Orient and the Middle East; these immigrants have come to live in "the States" and learn American English speech. Their influence has contributed to the changing character of the language. The speech pathologist will meet members of the immigrant group as he studies the problem of foreign accent.

Last in the list of languages of the New World is the "creolized-language" group. Negro speech influences are heard in several areas of the United States, but creolized speech, as defined by one authority, may not agree with the definition of a second authority. The subject is open to debate. The clinician will meet these influences in foreign accent frequently characterized as *substandard speech*.

Recent changes in American attitudes toward foreign-language study have led to the creation of a fifth influence on bilingualism and foreign accent for the United States. *Exchange students* and *professional* people in ever-increasing numbers are coming to this country for educational purposes. Each visitor brings his native speech and language patterns and a varying amount of American English speech. Many, anxious to learn to speak "native" American English, seek assistance in the speech classrooms of day schools or evening schools, in community programs or on university campuses, in clinics or at available American Language Institutes. You will be working with foreign accents heard in the speech of these students. Kozen Kanshiro came from Okinawa, Emery Korka from Hungary, Mariana Kanellus from Greece; each came seeking American speech for a different reason. Petite Mitsua Atashi, the superb violinist from Japan, and Hong Lee from China, the Ph.D. candidate in chemistry, wanted to learn English speech as well as to obtain advanced training in their fields of specialization. You will meet these stimulating people from other cultures, thanks to the new influence provided by student exchange programs and our widening view of world languages.

Nor is this a "one-way" process of language mixing. American students and professional specialists are traveling to all parts of the world as *seekers* rather than as tourists. Each candidate for such travel carries American English speech to the languages of the country visited. Some of you will be training members of the Peace Corps to communicate with a variety of different language groups throughout the world. According to reports of early returnees, soon after arriving in their assigned country, many of them were asked to teach natives to "speak American." One of the most useful methods of introducing these people to the principles and ideals we profess is to satisfy their curiosity about American English, and when requested, to teach them the principles of American speech. Your knowledge of foreign accent will assist you in this, since you will be teaching the principles of spoken English to those going into other language areas.

Interference will be found in the speech of the polyglot as a result of five influences, past and present: native-language influence, colonization, creolization of the native language, immigration, and foreign students and professional personnel-exchange work.

Children of the immigrants who came to the United States in the last ten years will be entering school. Language interference will usually be evident in the speech of a child raised in a bilingual atmosphere. The average child is unable to cope with the problem of maintaining true bilingual conditions by separating the forms and structures of the two languages. Polish, Hungarian, Serbian, and Belgian students taught in a public school in a Middle Western urban area might reflect the foreign accent described here. The native American Indians will appear in the classroom or the clinic of some of the readers of this text. Their language overlap is often trilingual with the "native" Indian tongue forming the base on which two other dialects have been superimposed with resulting "foreign accent" characteristics. Also among the native groups are those third-, fourth- or fifth-generation Americans who have been raised in an area where they hear the speech of only their localized dialect. This dialect may be classed as substandard in comparison with one of the major dialects of American English because of the creolizing influences exerted upon it by various environmental speech patterns. Finally, the speech pathologist and teacher will meet the influence of interference in the speech of the exchange student. Those visitors from schools or professions who come to America to profit by the advanced knowledge in special fields that can be obtained only in the United States frequently request assistance in learning to speak American English.

A. NATIVE LANGUAGE

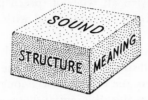

B. LANGUAGE CONTRASTS

NATIVE LANGUAGE   SECOND LANGUAGE

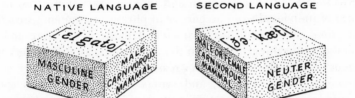

SPANISH   ENGLISH

C. TYPES OF BILINGUALS

COORDINATE BILINGUAL   COMPOUND BILINGUAL

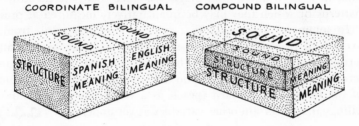

Figure 5. One Language and More.

Elements of Interference

Having evaluated the auditory and perceptive ability of the student or client, the clinician or teacher is now faced with the need for evaluating the motor production of speech elements. Detection of areas of need returns the speech pathologist to the clinical methods of differential diagnosis used consistently with other problems

14   You have met "differential diagnosis" before in your work as a clinician and teacher. Myklebust (110:78-128) related the method to language-impaired children.

in the speech or audiology clinic. The symptoms of the polyglot condition may sound the same when first heard, and the label *foreign accent* is frequently used to apply to all types of speech problems from true foreignism to the speech of the individual with cerebral palsy.

Differential diagnosis begins with the recording of speech samples of a previously prepared test, constructed to analyze the various elements of the speech produced by the client. First among the elements of speech to be scrutinized in this differential diagnosis is the pattern of *sound* related to the individual phonemes of the second language. Second is the speech evidence of nonphonemic sound patterns such as *intonation,* pitch and intensity variation, *stress* in the form of individual word accents or in phrase and sentence structure, and *time* evidences in the character of pause or juncture and the number of meaningful units in the time frame, as well as the superfluous sounds added for various reasons. Third, the structure of the *grammar,* word positions, and syntax of the individual's speech should be analyzed for study. Finally, word confusions and *meaning,* idiomatic statements, and semantic implications that have been distorted by interference are to be evaluated. This will be the most difficult area in differential diagnosis, since there are no structural patterns by which they may be quantitatively measured at present.

In summary, we can say that *interferences* may result from the overlap of two speech systems, a primary language pattern and a secondary language pattern. The character and amount of interference present will depend upon the languages involved, the ability of the individual to learn speech as a coordinate or a compound bilingual, and certain other variables as yet undefined.

INTRODUCTION

AS WE SPEAK A SECOND LANGUAGE, THE TANGLED SUBSTANCE OF OUR TALK
leads to confusion. The listener smiles, then puzzled looks appear;
confusion, embarrassment, or laughter frequently follow. As a
speaker, we are not understood and the message that we hoped to
convey is lost in sound that no longer communicates meaning.

If we are to study the accent of Manuel Ruiz, we must begin with
an individual idiolect, the communicator's speech. The dialect of
Spanish which Manuel has always heard and spoken must be considered, for the sound patterns will be characteristic of one of the
dialects of Spanish. Conversely, if we are to study the second lan-

3 *characteristics of foreign accent*

guage which gives Manuel his difficulty, we must select one of the
dialects of American English.

Why choose General American dialect in preference to any other
dialect? The answer to this question will determine the clinician's
approach to foreign accent. Will it be traditional or linguistic? The
author would choose this particular dialect of American English for
discussion because it is the speech to which he has been exposed
throughout his life, not because the speech is in any way more logical, efficient, or acceptable than any other dialect of American English.

Speech is for use in oral communication and the idiolect of any
individual should be that form of speech which is most useful and
efficient for his needs in a communicative situation. The appropri-
ateness of the speech we use should be determined by the needs of

15　There is a disagreement between formal grammarians or traditional
grammarians and linguists, speech specialists, and language teachers
regarding the "usage" of English. Hall (52:9-29) presents one side of
the story on this choice between "right and wrong." Follett (42:175-80)
attacks what he calls *bargain basement English* which, he contends, is

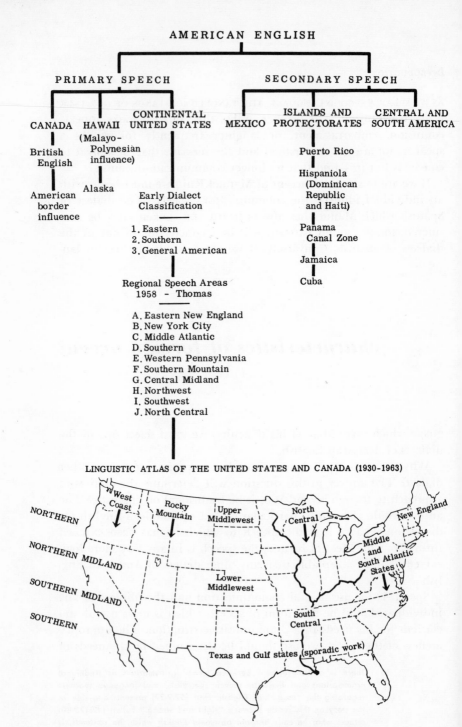

Figure 6. Geographical Chart of American English.

the product of the "new rhetoric." Evans (35:185-90) responds to Follett in defense of the modern approach to English usage.

the communication situation. A clinician or teacher should teach useful language.

Manuel Ruiz speaks his dialect of Spanish for the same reason that you speak yours. It was the speech heard and practiced as a child and as a maturing adult. The "correctness" of that dialect is important to us only in that it provides the base for a contrasting *second* language. What is significant to the clinician is that he be able to determine the structure of that dialect. He must investigate three basic features: (*a*) the *sound system* used by the native speaker of the language to which the dialect belongs, (*b*) the *structural grammar* elements, word, and syntax, and (*c*) the *semantic setting* of the total culture pattern that is reflected in the speaker's language.

Results of scientific research and analysis conducted on language assist the therapist in locating those points of sound difference which appear when English and the native dialect are compared.

16   Are you wondering where you can ever find information concerning the language background of the many students you may see in the school or university clinic? Bower (11) provides an excellent start for seeking such information. *Language Learning,* a magazine publication of the University of Michigan, provides materials on all languages with excellent suggestions for the teacher and therapist.

Acceptance of one standard of speech for use as a first or second language is based not on logic or order in the language universe, but on the political, cultural, and economic factors operating in that community in which it is used. The popularity of various languages on the international scene reflects this conviction. H. L. Mencken presents the changing condition in 1936 as he says:

"The English tongue is of small reach, stretching no further than this island of ours, nay not there over all."
This was written in 1582, the writer was Richard Mulcaster, headmaster of the Merchant Taylors' School, teacher of prosody to Edmund Spencer, and one of the earliest English grammarians. At the time he wrote, English was spoken by between four and five million people, and stood fifth among the European languages with French, German, Italian, and Spanish ahead of it in the order and Russian following. Two hundred years later Italian had dropped behind but Russian had gone ahead, so that English was still in fifth place. But by the end of the Eighteenth Century it began to move forward, and by the middle of the Nineteenth Century it had forced its way into first place. Today it is so far in the lead that it is probably spoken by as many people as the next two European languages—Russian and German combined (*100*).

This statement was written twenty-two years ago and since that time English has greatly increased its world-wide use. Pei (115) shows that Spanish has taken the place of German among the European languages. English still leads the European group with a total of 250 million and is surpassed only by Chinese with 600 million. The significance of English speech in the world will make it the first choice as a second language for millions of people. The prestige value of a first-place language, as well as the scientific, economic, and cultural information that the United States communicates, makes it a logical choice.

Any language sought as a secondary or target language will be that one which has most utility for the seeker. The dialect he learns will be determined by the place in which he seeks assistance. If he goes to England to learn English, he will speak British dialect. Eight Somali boys came to a university to do advanced study. During the first week of their presence on campus there were comments by local American students that they could not be understood, yet they spoke English. The sounds were there, but the pattern was noticeably different and the few additional changes in sound elements confused the listeners. When evaluated for a speech class, they were found to speak polyglot English. The confusion of British English with their native Somaliland dialects rendered the speech unintelligible for the average General American listener.

If we are to teach English for oral communication as a second language, we should choose that form of speech which will be most useful to the second-language learner.

Speech Defined

Speech is communication that utilizes audible and visible symbols to accomplish its purpose. Communication is defined as the transfer of materials, information, and ideas from a producer or source to a receiver or destination utilizing a transmitting system or medium of some type. For the clinician who meets the extremely hard-of-

17   Berlo (6:23-30) presents speech in terms of the communication process. Simon (128:199-200) defines it for speech pathologists and audiologists. Contrast these definitions with those used by linguists such as Hockett (64:393) and Trager (139:1-12).

hearing or deaf individual, child or adult, in the classroom or clinic, the need for using gesture and movement in teaching lip reading, sign language, finger spelling, or some combined code becomes a demand of the "speech" situation. When you watch the aphasoid child or the emotionally disturbed child in the evaluation room, you soon discover the need for including movement and gesture in the concept of speech as a form of communication.

Speech is the result of kinetic action. Movements of the entire body are related to the speech act. This bodily activity which accompanies the production of sound symbols exists as a part of the speech act. Varying cultures have varying patterns of action and gesture which accompany speaking. These are as much a part of speech for communication as are the sound symbols themselves. The Bulgarian shakes his head vertically rather than horizontally for "No!" Our concept of speech thus must include these visual patterns of movement which complement the sound symbols and often render them intelligible.

Sounds of Speech

As speech is produced it flows as a pattern of sound in a dynamic whole. If it is unduly fractionated for any reason, the speech tends to call attention to itself.

18   The stutterer has such breaks in the flow pattern of speech, and Sheehan
      (126:474-82) designates these breaks as one of the most important
      evidences of stuttering. Wendahl and Cole (148:281-86) oppose the the-
      ory that stuttering can be evaluated on the basis of the "blocks."

If we assume that speech is a dynamic flow of sounds, then we must conclude that one sound will influence another. Therefore, the ideal situation in which to study foreign accent would be conducted within the frame of the dynamic flow of sound. Linguists, chemists, physicists, even psychologists, extract a sample and make generalizations from the study of many samples in this same way. We will, in discussing the characteristics of foreign accent, extract a sample and assemble a sufficient number of samples from which a generalization can be made.

Phonemes

Because the sample of speech is drawn and others have completed the job for us, we will discover that American English utilizes a combination of sounds that have been classified in three divisions: vowel sounds, consonant sounds, and diphthong sounds or blends. The phoneme provides a starting point for our evaluation of the speech of the second-language student. We will need a chart of the sounds of his native language. Figure 7 demonstrates one method of

CONSONANTS

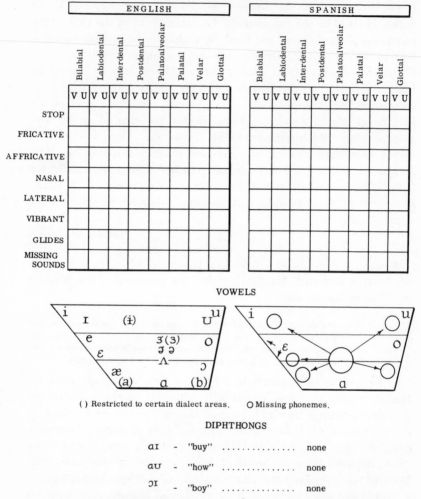

Figure 7. Comparative Chart of English and Spanish Phonemes.

( ) Restricted to certain dialect areas.   O Missing phonemes.

VOWELS

DIPHTHONGS

aɪ - "buy" .... none

aʊ - "how" .... none

ɔɪ - "boy" .... none

setting up the comparison for the therapist. Transparent overlays might be helpful in working out the preliminary contrasts of sounds in the two languages. If you have large groups of students with problems originating in the same language or with similar dialects of the same language, it will be advisable to prepare such comparison sheets for *each* language.

Sounds of the two languages should be compared for similarities and differences. *First,* those phonemes present in both languages could be compared. If they are identical in all features, there will probably be no evidence of foreign accent related to these sounds. *Second,* even though certain sounds are represented by the same phonetic symbol, they may differ in production or acoustic details. These will create foreign-accent problems. *Third,* for those sounds missing in the second language which exist in the native language, we can expect some type of sound substitution or distortion. In the medial position, the Navajo speaker learning English will substitute [d] for the sound of [ð] in such words as *mother* and *father.* In the initial position the [tx] sound, an unvoiced velar stop followed by a velar aspirant of Navajo, will frequently be substituted for both sounds. This sound appears in Navajo only in the initial position and is heard in that position in English in such words as *thin* and *then,* even though the initial sounds on these words represent two distinct phonemes of English, [θ] in *th*in and [ð] in *th*en. Finally, for sounds that are present in the native language but missing from the second language there will be a problem of possible additions. In German, the final *e* of such words as *Buche, Sprache,* and *keusche* is produced as [ə], the schwa sound. When American English words end in an *e,* the sound seldom is produced. Two speech problems appear. First, the native German frequently adds a schwa sound to words such as *like* and *ache,* following his native habit of producing these sounds in the final position. Second, the schwa sound is added to such words as *book, speak,* and *cook,* probably because there is similarity between the sound pattern and word meaning of the English and German. In class you will hear the supernumerary [ə] at the end of American English words produced by native German speakers. It can also be heard at the beginning of words of English that begin with [s] when the speaker has a native Spanish background.

Discriminating Auditory Details

Having compared the phoneme systems of the two languages, American English and the native language of your student, for *major* differences in phonemes, you will want to know all the variations of sound production in the two types of phonemes. This step includes comparison of the sounds represented by similar I.P.A. symbols in the two languages.

Even though two sounds are phonemically similar, there are often certain phonetic differences in their production which should be noted by the instructor. In Russian the sounds [t], [d], and [n] are dentals; in English they are alveolars. This creates a problem for the Russian student learning English. In the clinic and in the classroom the dental form of [d] will be heard in such words as *lady, ladder,* and *candle.*

The importance of understanding such allophonic variants within the phoneme structure of the two languages cannot be overemphasized. It may help you to explain some of those tantalizing sound distortions that are heard in foreign accents but which cannot be located by making phoneme comparisons in the two languages.

Distribution

As every therapist knows, the sounds of any language are distributed according to the pattern of the language in which they appear. Certain sounds appear at the beginning of the word, in the initial position, while others never appear in this distribution. In English the [ŋ] phoneme never appears in the initial position, but in other languages, such as Nbanga, an African language, the sound regularly appears in the initial position.

Similarly, the sounds of any language appear in the medial and final positions. Our study of articulation problems indicates certain positions in which children and adults have more difficulty than others in producing the sounds required for the language spoken. Not only will these sounds appear in the beginning, middle, or end

19   Does the therapist need to know the research on sound acquisition in relation to position in a sound complex to do efficient clinical or classroom work? Milisen (102) reviews the early studies on articulation and presents results of work with his students. Keenan (79:171-74) presents an argument for abandoning the initial, medial, and final classification.

of a word, but they will also appear in certain relationships with all the other sounds. There will be questions. Will the vowel *o* appear before every other consonant in English? Will it appear before or after every other vowel? A number of other similar questions are to be answered by the clinician working with foreign accent. The distribution of the phonemes of the native language should also be known and available for comparison. Such details of preparation on the part of the clinician will provide the base from which work can begin with the student. No speech pathologist need fear that he will be required to prepare all of the comparative analyses needed in this preliminary planning since descriptive linguists have provided charts of the various sound systems. Occasionally there will be a need to translate some of the linguists' symbols, but you will find the majority are fairly consistent with the I.P.A.

To summarize the preparation for evaluating a foreign-accent problem:

1. Prepare a comparison of the "segmental" phonemes of the language.
2. List the *variations* or individual features of these phonemes for both languages.
3. Develop a chart of *arrangement* or *distribution* of these phonemes in each language.

Hearing the Sounds of Speech

In first-language learning, gross sounds, meaningful environmental sounds, then language sounds are heard and then organized for use. In second-language learning and in work with foreign accent, the order of learning is no less important. One of the characteristics of foreign accent is the inability of the individual habituated in patterns of his native language to hear the fine differences present in the sound patterns of a second language. Evaluation of this discrimination ability for our student is the next step following the comparison of sound systems in the two languages.

Testing Discrimination

The basic purpose of this testing should be to discover the possible auditory "trouble spots." To accomplish this we use the *minimal contrasts* of sound patterns. For example, if we are interested in knowing whether Peter Marcus could distinguish between the sounds represented by the phonemes [i] and [ɪ], which are separate phonemes in English but are allophones of the same phonemes in Spanish, we might contrast these sounds arranged in a pattern such as that presented below.

	A	B	C
1.	[mim]	[mim]	[mɪm]
2.	[im] or [ima]	[ɪm] or [ɪma]	[im] or [ima]
3.	[dɪ] or [adɪ]	[di] or [adi]	[di] or [adi]

Peter would be asked to designate, in each group, which two syllables sounded the same to him. This could be completed in oral response or in written response, because the selection can be indicated by a check and need not involve any language associations. In the example presented, number 1, the correct response, would be syllables A and B; in number 2, letters A and C would be checked; and in number 3, letters B and C should be checked to indicate that a difference was heard. Numbers of patterns could be developed by the clinician to test the ability of the listener to discriminate between the sounds selected for use in minimal contrasts. Each phoneme should be tested in the various positions in which it is used in English—initial, medial, and final.

Syllables, words, and sentences have been used for testing minimal contrasts in audiology and speech pathology, as well as in psychology and linguistics. In some tests, both words are produced for matching with a previously produced model. Other methods require a choice when the printed list is available to the student being tested. A third technique is the use of multiple choice in which three or more samples are presented with one of the list being different. In this, the subject is to choose those which are similar or to select the one variant. Frequently, as in the case of phonetically balanced (PB) word lists, the listener is required to match the word produced with a model in his language repertory. Valid arguments are available for using each of the methods suggested. The technique selected by the clinician will depend upon the needs of the teacher and the student.

At the University of Puerto Rico an evaluation system for perceiving minimal sound contrasts has been developed and used with students of Spanish-language background learning English as a second language. Tucker (142) developed paragraph materials to supplement the test patterns available in words and sentences. Such material provides work in discrimination of sounds in context. Instructors working with foreign accent may find these materials useful for assisting Spanish-language students with sound discrimination in context.

As the testing of sound perception moves from nonsense syllables to meaningful contextual materials, additional variables are included in the testing situation. By varying the conditions and controlling different variables, the therapist or teacher can obtain several types of information to be used in his work with foreign accent.

20   Remember the problem you had when trying to learn the Spanish r's; that odd German sound in *nacht;* or the special resonance for *bon* in French? Students with a foreign accent frequently have difficulty with the American *schwa* [ə] sound. Kantner and West (77:92-6) present an interpretation of the schwa concept.

The *first* major characteristic of foreign accent is the inability of the student of a second language to make necessary fine auditory discriminations when hearing a new speech pattern. The same difficulty will be discovered in considering intonation and stress patterns of speech or structural patterns and grammar, as well as meanings associated with each of these contrasts. We must always remember that the foreign student has been habituated to the sounds of each characteristic of language and speech and that the perceptions of new relationships must be taught in progressive steps in order to build the foundations for speech production.

Speech production

The major emphasis in foreign accent has always been on the element of *produced* speech. Spoken language gives us the symptom of the polyglot condition with which we will be working in the classroom or clinic. The evidence of foreign accent is what is produced by the speaker and heard by the listener. Knowledge and automatic control of sound patterns are the basis of speech production.

American English Sounds

Each language has a set of phonemes which are distinctive for use in that language and which may be compared or contrasted with the sound of any other language. The same sounds may be present in both languages and may be represented by a common orthographic symbol. The opposite extreme may exist; the sound, present in one speech pattern, may be missing in the second language. A third condition exists when the two sounds are present in both languages but represented by two different orthographic symbols, or one sound is an allophone of another phoneme in the second language. In Spanish and English the [p] phoneme is represented by the same written symbol; the allophonic characteristics of the sounds in the two languages may vary slightly in relation to other sounds, but the distinctive character of the sound causes no difficulty for the native Spanish speaker learning English speech. Second, the [x] sound used in Spanish does not exist as a phoneme in American English. The student learning Spanish must introduce himself to an entirely new set of articulatory habits. Finally, there are many examples of the third classification of problems in Spanish and English. The [r] phoneme in Spanish presents two variations, both of

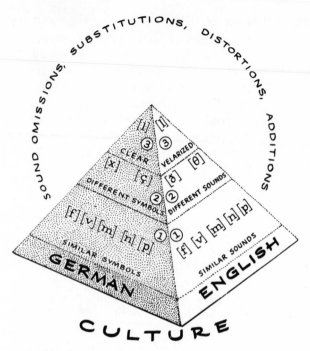

Figure 8. Foreign Accent—The Sounds. 1. Similar sounds; similar orthographic symbols. 2. Different sounds; same orthographic symbols. 3. Same phoneme; same orthographic symbol; allophones give variant sounds.

which are different in production from the American English [r]; among the vowels the [ɪ] and [u] phonemes of English are allophones of Spanish phonemes but are not used to distinguish words in Spanish. When the student with Spanish-language background attempts to speak General American English, he will encounter difficulty recognizing and producing the phonemes in words such as *sit* and *pool* as distinctive from *seat* and *pull*.

The first group of sounds, those that appear to be exactly the same in both languages, should be scrutinized carefully, since the differences between two language sound systems are subtle. Such a trap is provided by the Spanish [b] and the English [b]. It is best to rely on the research work of the acoustical psychologist and the linguist for this information; we can make practical use of their research in both the clinic and classroom.

In the second group of sounds most important is the *schwa* of American English, [ə], for many foreign students have never heard

this sound either as a variant of one of their native-language phonemes or as a distinctive sound pattern. A second example of this
characteristic of foreign accent is illustrated by the absence of the
[ʃ] sound in Spanish as a phoneme; the [tʃ] is frequently substituted
for the American English sound in the word *shoe,* leading to a confusion with the word *chew.* In the last category, the sounds which
are similar in orthographic characteristics but have different function, distribution or other details are the [b] and the [v] phonemes.

We will assume that the first- and second-language learners have
the same speech-producing mechanism and are capable of learning
the sound patterns of either language. The facility with which they
learn the second language will be influenced by the characteristics
of age, maturation of the physiological and neurological system, verbal facility, motivation, and the system by which the language is
taught. The speech of the individual will vary in proportion to the
types of "approximations" which he makes in his attempts to reproduce the sound system of the new language. The job of the clinician
is to specify those approximations and to develop the distinctive
acoustic features of the sound patterns which will be regarded as
"native" by the listener who speaks the language.

> 21   Cartright (24:313-17) presents the case for the "speech lab" as a means
> of supplying native models to approximate. Harms (56:214-19) suggests
> that programmed learning might be used in speech as well as in other
> subjects.

Structural Characteristics

In the dynamic process which is speech, the sounds of language
are blended together in words. The linguists say these words are
composed of *morphemes* which are the smallest unit of meaningful
expression used to form words in any language. Such a structure may
include either a single sound such as [s] in the case of *book-s,* the
characteristic sign of plurality, or a syllable such as *book* in the
illustration. In various languages the characteristic structure of

> 22   Nida (113:3-106) offers the most thorough description of the area
> called morphology. For the clinician, Hughes (69) describes the mor-
> pheme and relates it to the sound characteristics of a meaningful unit
> of language.

words will depend upon historical background of the language and
the culture in which it is used. There are some languages that do
not have word types. The linguist prefers to say that morphemes are

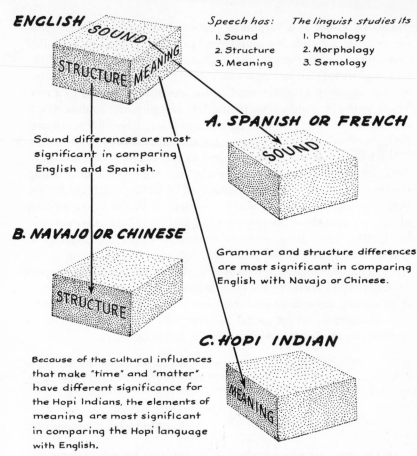

Speech has: *The linguist studies its*
1. Sound   1. Phonology
2. Structure   2. Morphology
3. Meaning   3. Semology

Sound differences are most
significant in comparing
English and Spanish.

A. SPANISH OR FRENCH

B. NAVAJO OR CHINESE

Grammar and structure differences
are most significant in comparing
English with Navajo or Chinese.

C. HOPI INDIAN

Because of the cultural influences
that make "time" and "matter"
have different significance for
the Hopi Indians, the elements of
meaning are most significant
in comparing the Hopi language
with English.

Figure 9. Characteristics of Foreign Accent Language Interference.

the ingredients from which any utterance is built. It is not essential that the student know the theory of morphemic structure in order to rebuild his foreign accent, but the more his instructor or therapist understands about the speech characteristics of the two languages, the more progress will be made.

Word Arrangement

Our present concern lies in the use of words as they appear in the flow pattern of speech. English has developed a sequential pattern of words to which the native speaker of the language has become accustomed. Other languages have comparable patterns of arrangement.

First, the native and second language may have structural patterns used in speech which are identical: English, "I see the dog"; French, "Je vois le chien." The subject, verb, and object arrangement is similar, and the speaker of French would have little difficulty with the word arrangement of English in such a sentence. There are other arrangements which would cause difficulty if transferred directly into English. For example, the "delayed attribute" in German provides a problem for most native English learners, because the literal translation of the word distorts the sentence sense. A caution similar to that presented in relation to the sounds of the language should be reiterated. The surface similarity of two speech patterns does not guarantee similarity in all points of structure and grammar; each item must be compared individually. Here we can depend upon the linguists for the comparative information.

Second, the structural patterns of the two languages may be so different that movement from one to another will require the acquisition of two entirely different syntactical forms. Confusion may result while learning the two language patterns, but they are relatively easy to keep separate once they have been assimilated. Learning this entirely new arrangement of sound is comparable to the familiar problem of producing familiar sounds in unfamiliar positions in speech therapy.

Even though the words have meaning and may be understood, the arrangement in which they are placed can present a major problem in formulation for the speaker of English as a second language. He says to himself, "How shall I say that the flower is of blue color?" "Shall I say, a flower blue, or a blue flower?" The choice will depend upon the speaker's background. The English speaker is accustomed to the use of a class of words known as *adjectives*. The absence of a closely corresponding class of words in Navajo may create a problem at first for the Navajo student. He must learn to use certain words as adjectives. Then, the next problem becomes learning the appropriate position of the adjective in the sentence and the use of various adjectives to reveal alternate shades of meaning in English.

Third, the words or structures may have some resemblance to the native language but are deceptive because of the fine differentiations present. Cognates are often carried over from one language to the other because they sound alike in production; however, the meaning may be entirely different for the two languages. An example of such confusion is contained in the word *language* of French. The English listener translates it *language,* but the French differentiate between *language* and *langue* in reference to *speech* and *language.* Homophonous words become confused when the meaning in the second language differs radically from that in the first. Often the distortion in production of a single phoneme will add to this confusion. Your visits with Hyman Kaplan will verify this.

In addition to mastering the meaning of words and to learning their appropriate location is the problem of directly translating the syntactical form into the speech of the second language. Word order differs among languages and the student must learn American English sentence arrangements. Among the examples cited earlier were some from Indian children learning English as a second language; the examples contained these ideas: "I have a long hair," "I am so in quick to town," and "My mother is clean the floor." Most of the words are present to express the basic meaning in English, but the missing words and the arrangement of the words leads the listener to say, "He speaks with a foreign accent."

The intricate relationships which exist between the structure of a language and the cultural background of the individual speaking that language will be clarified in Chapter 7 when we discuss the details of foreign accent as revealed in the patterns of speech of the second-language learner. Our chief concern will be with the reduction of this accent by finding the points of similarity and difference in the two language structures which lead to the substitution of native speech sounds, patterns of expression, intonation, stress, and meaning in the American English speech of the student. Whorf (*151*:28-37) has brought out the significance of the cultural background for the speaker and his speech in his discussion of Hopi concepts of "time" and "matter." The clinician cannot hope to assist

23   The Whorf theory of language and life has influenced the patterns of
     speech therapy as well as of linguistics. See Whorf (*151*) for his early
     formulation of principles and Whorf (*149*) for his assembled ideas.

the student with a foreign accent unless he is willing to understand the culture which stands behind and within the native speaker and comes out with his speech. The silent language gives us further cues to the need for understanding the *full* pattern of speech in order to assist with foreign accent.   ♫♫♫

WHEN YOU STAND IN THE LOBBY OF INTERNATIONAL HOUSE, SNATCHES OF conversation are heard from groups of students clustered in various parts of the reception room. One group is speaking Japanese, the Tokyo dialect taught in Japanese schools. From the opposite side of the hall, beside the fireplace, comes a contrasting melody pattern in conversation. Stephen Kovacs is the center of this group. A refugee who came to the United States during the Hungarian crisis, he remained to work as an instructor in the laboratory. Patterns of pitch change can be heard in this speech, but they are not those of the Japanese students nor those of that group of American English visitors who are asking for assistance at the information desk.

4

melody and intonation in foreign accent

Each of these languages has a different melody pattern when heard in connected speech. When native speakers of Japanese or Hungarian attempt to learn English, their speech habits will interfere with the acquisition of a new intonation pattern of English. For the Japanese student an accented syllable will signal the need for a slight rise in pitch, while for the American English student this accent usually indicates the need for increased emphasis or intensity of sound. As the Hungarian student attempts to chain the words of American English, he reproduces his native accent on the first syllable of each word. If each of these students carries over his native habits of intonation, they will speak with a foreign accent, even if all the phonemes are uttered perfectly.

Acquiring Melody in Speech

What the infant hears when he first emerges from his welter of silence is the noise pattern of the world about him. His own birth cry is added to the confusion of sound in which he is enveloped during that first hour of life. Noises of the nursery become a part of the language melody of his new world. Out of this confusion come bubbling rivulets of sound soon to be identified as speech. As the child experiments with sound, melodies appear in his own mouth similar to those repeated by his parents and friends. It is in this osmotic fashion, through absorption, that the melody of American English speech becomes a part of the speech of the child.

The second-language learner becomes the product of a similar early training, but not in English. In his own native language he has absorbed the changing intonation patterns of his parents and associates as automatic reactions. When he seeks to speak the language of his new culture, these deeply ingrained habits of pitch change intrude. His native melody "shows through" and we say he has a foreign accent.

Melody and Intonation of American English

American English consists of a flow of sound and, as such, has melody. The melody of speech and the melody of song are similar but provide contrasting characteristics. Both are symbolic systems; one uses words as symbols, while the other uses musical notes as well as words for expressing the idea contained in the communication. Each has a pattern that can be recognized by the listener. It is in their contrasts that speech and song differ fundamentally. In musical compositions the melody has been established, and there is little allowance for innovation or freedom of expression if the pattern is to be recognized. In speech, on the contrary, flexibility of pattern in expression of any given idea is not only permitted, but it is encouraged. Thus, the speaker becomes an innovator once he has command of his intonation design and his materials for melody. In this the speaker might be compared to the participant in the musical "jam session" in which innovation is encouraged.

Definition of Melody and Intonation

The terms *melody* and *intonation* are used interchangeably by some authorities in the areas of speech, foreign language, linguistics, and psychology to refer to the variations in pitch pattern used in any stream of speech. Others assign special characteristics to melody

24   Sarett, Foster, and Sarett (124) make melody one of the three characteristics of speech and build their entire discussion of communication for informative or emotional stimulation on the basis of *melody, time,* and *force.*

by designating it as the pitch pattern used "to mark larger units, such as phrases or clauses," or a "contour of melody" making one form subordinate to the other. For our discussion in foreign accent we will consider the *melody* of the speech pattern as *that over-all pattern of the prosodic elements of speech which include pitch, quality, strength, and duration* assigned by Carrell and Tiffany (*21*) as "those variables which add the 'plus' values to communication."

Intonation in speech will here be considered the *pattern of changing pitch in voice used to give meaning to the word or words spoken.* Included in the pitch considerations will be inflectional variations, step changes of pitch, and sound diminutions accompanied by falling pitch levels used in American English to signal the end of a clause or a "terminal juncture."

Each of the characteristics of pitch change has a visual symbol which may be used to indicate the character and direction of pitch change. From the available methods of representing intonation, a subject about which there is much controversy, we will be using a system of numbers, plus contour lines and arrows.

> **25** Visual symbol systems for indicating intonation and melody changes are as varied as the opinions on most other factors of speech analysis. Fairbanks (*36*) devotes two chapters, Chapters 11 and 14, to pitch and its relation to intonation; he offers a simplified notation system that some therapists favor. Bolinger (*9:199-210*) disagrees with the analysis system offered by most linguists and offers challenging comments on the evaluation of intonation and melody in speech.

Use of Numbers

In the number system, number 1 represents the very lowest level of pitch used by any speaker. Number 2 will signify the normal "monotone" voice pitch used as a base by most speakers of English. The next higher level of intonation contour will be represented by the number 3, and the *very high* pitch used occasionally in excitement or exclamation will be designated by number 4. The intonation pattern of Japanese speech gives a contrasting melodic tone, using only pitch elevation to signal emphasis instead of increased intensity or force as in English. This causes the Japanese speaker to sound as though he is moving into the upper (number 4) area of pitch levels much more frequently than does the American English speaker. Most authorities signify that pitch levels are relative rather than absolute among speakers; this same characteristic of relativity may exist in languages as well if we compare the over-all pitch patterns of Japanese and Chinese with American English. At least to the ear of the native American listener, the tonal pitch sounds higher and the intonational variation more restricted in area number 1.

An example of the use of numbers to designate pitch levels may be illustrated by the following sentence:

$$\overset{2}{\text{I am}} \quad \overset{3}{\text{here.}}$$

For the student who has some difficulty handling the language in its oral form and who has had little experience with the written character of the language, such a number system might add to his confusion rather than simplify the problem. For this reason, marks above and below the line, as well as angular or curved lines through syllables or words indicating pitch levels and their changes, are frequently used to show the contour of intonation.

Contour Lines

A contour line is a series of dots or a solid line that illustrates the changing pattern of pitch levels employed in an intonation pattern. The line may be either continuous or broken and direction arrows may be employed to show continuing direction of pitch change. Two simple contour lines are illustrated below.

$$\underset{2}{\text{I am}} \; \overset{3}{\underline{\text{here.}}} \qquad \text{or} \qquad \underset{2}{\text{I am here.}} \; \underset{1}{\rule{0pt}{0pt}}$$

It often becomes necessary to indicate the breaks in intonation pattern found in such statements as:

$$\underset{2}{\text{Not}} \; \overset{3}{\underline{\text{now.}}} \qquad \text{or} \qquad \underset{2}{\text{Not}} \; \underset{1}{\text{now!}}$$

Notice the contour line is broken to indicate a "step" change in pitch level which contrasts with an inflectional change that is continuous in one direction. The same words might be spoken as a question:

$$\underset{2}{\text{Not no}} \overset{3}{\diagup \text{w?}}$$

Change Within Words

As illustrated above by the diagonal line through the syllable, the inflectional change takes place in the middle of the word *now*. Such pitch changes within words of a sentence are popular in American English speech. Associated with emphasis on the word being spoken, the slide from one pitch level to another makes a distinctive feature of American speech melody with which the speaker of most foreign languages will have difficulty. Books on speech training often contain a sentence of three words asking the student to produce the words in such a way as to give nine or ten different meanings. This is accomplished by using variations in inflection and emphasis. One such sentence is:

Some texts use a curved line to give the visual pattern of variable change in pitch on words for which the inflectional variation appears. If this method of picturing inflectional changes is adopted,

26 The clinician often has difficulty finding materials for use on the intonation phase of foreign accent. Slager (*130*) and his associates have developed a series of six graded texts for teaching English as a foreign language. Sections on pronunciation provide useful material for the speech clinician as well as for the teacher. Gordon and Wong (*48*) provide contour patterns for intonation and melody.

the contour would look like this:

Significance of the angular and curved lines is the same when used to demonstrate pitch change within the word. Some authorities utilize the curved line because the visual cue assists the student with foreign accent to sense the glide characteristic more effectively. Angular lines will be used in this text.

A final indicator of intonation that will assist the clinician by visually representing pitch change in voice is the arrow. Since the arrow is a signal that is commonly used for direction, it is easily understood and very useful for demonstration purposes in foreign accent. Three directional arrows are used: vertical up ↑, vertical down ↓, and horizontal ⟶. The only variation in use of these three indicators is in attachment or nonattachment of the arrow to the intonation contour. The following sentences illustrate the use of the number 4 pitch level used in excitement or in enthusiastic speech, as well as two methods of utilizing arrows.

Uniformity of usage is essential. All members of the staff might profitably adopt an acceptable system. Only one caution seems necessary—that this system be reasonably well known to permit the student to translate the symbols into other systems to his advantage. The method should be so simple that it proves to be an assistance in producing American English speech and not a distraction or complicating factor.

Fries (44) states that peeople who speak Portuguese and Spanish as a native language use an intonation pattern curve which varies from very low at the beginning of the sentence through a series of rising levels of pitch in the middle, to very low at the end of the sentence. When the number system adopted for this text is used (number 1 representing the lowest pitch level and numbers 2 and 3 the rising levels in intonation) the Portuguese speaker of English would have a 1—1 pattern. He would begin at the lowest level, pass through levels 2 and 3, perhaps even use level 4, and return to level 1 in speaking the sentence. Such intonation contrasts with the commonly used intonation pattern of American English when statements are spoken. The English pattern revealed by research is 3—1. The sentence begins on a rather high level and ends at the low pitch level. These contrasts can be illustrated by the following sentences:

Although there are variations in patterns of intonation and melody produced when different people say the same phrase or when the sentence is spoken on different occasions, Pike found these to be the most consistent configurations. When declarative statements were spoken the Portuguese and Spanish students used a 1—1 pattern and the 3—1 pattern was used by the majority of American English speakers. Portuguese and Spanish students who are learning English speech tend to transfer their intonation patterns to the second language and will be regarded as having a foreign accent.

Assisting the Student with Intonation

Since we speak with our whole body and communicate by visual stimuli as well as by sounds produced in language, it is important to introduce our students to the total speech problem.

Watch the orchestra director when you attend your next symphony concert. His entire body moves to the melody of the selection as he guides the musicians through the intricacies of the score. Similarly, the violinists, cellists, violist, and tympany and percussionist "throw" themselves into the work at hand. Our students can develop a feeling for the melody and intonation of General American speech by participating in meaningful situations in which the patterns of melody are associated with General American speech.

1. Begin with a single word such as *Oh*. Have the group, two or many, imitate the various inflection patterns in chorus. Adult students often resist at first but soon adapt to the relaxed approach

necessary if flexibility is to be obtained. Body movements should be utilized to emphasize the inflection patterns. After the hands and arms trace these rising and falling patterns, get the students on their feet and employ total body movement.

2. Using familiar words such as *No* and *Yes,* explain the implications contained in various forms of inflection when questions are asked with these words. Demonstrate the emphatic use of descending pitch and stress. Practice in chorus work with individual questions and responses. "Are you going to the dance with Peter Erhart?" In a college group the girls will enjoy responding with different intonations in terms of your description of Peter as a football hero, a scholarly student, or a charming dancer.

3. Chanted syllables may be used to indicate the rising and falling intonation patterns used in connected speech. If your experiences are similar to those of the writer, you will find that foreign students have extreme difficulty in reproducing intonation patterns when more than one word is involved. After unison practice is used, try individual responses, being careful to keep the mood light and enthusiastic to avoid embarrassing the students.

4. For students who experience extreme difficulty, binaural stimulation has been used effectively by Van Riper (*144*:467-71). This provides an immediately available model if the student can hear himself in one ear and the instructor in the other.

5. Beginning practice should include only simple one-syllable words, nonsense syllables and babbling, reproduction of pauses, stress patterns, rhythms reproduced with fingers, hands and feet, as well as variation in pitch and melody. Since meaning is imparted

to American English by these variations in quality of sound, length of sound and silence, pitch patterns, and loudness patterns, the student needs to sense them as a totality of body reaction just as they learned their native language in total reactions as a child.

6. The *echo speech* technique also suggested by Van Riper can be used to train the student to echo automatically and simultaneously what is said by the instructor. When this is completed on the "after beat" without time for recall, the pattern becomes automatic. This is what we hope to acquire in second-language learning. Speech patterns need to become automatic in intonation and melody as well as in all other sound features.

7. As the practice progresses, the instructor may soften his production in binaural practice until the student is capable of producing the patterns alone.

8. Recording, listening to, and producing assigned patterns of intonation can be used at this point. The two-channel tape recorder offers the possibility of immediate-following, or "echo," techniques.

9. Van Riper (*144*:467-71) suggests that the student be assigned tasks such as echoing television or motion picture speakers until he has developed "simultaneous" speaking ability.

10. Visual patterns indicating direction of change and intonation contours will be useful in group activity after individual practice has accomplished the establishment of patterns desired.

STRUCTURE OF INTONATION

Pitch change and emphasis are closely related, and in describing the *center* of an intonation phrase we must refer to the highest point of stress in the phrase. Such a point marks the "beat" of the intonation unit and gives the language spoken the rhythm which is more regular in some languages than in others. Rise in pitch usually accompanies such stress points in English although it is not necessarily a requirement.

Because most center points in a stream of sound have an approach phase or onset phase and a decay phase or "fade out" phase, the entire structure has been called an *intonation phrase*. The intona-

---

27   Hockett (63) and Lado (85) describe these characteristics for use in speech analysis. Carrell and Tiffany (21) apply the principles to foreign accent.

tion phrase is marked by a primary stress at its center plus an introductory pitch level and a configuration of pitch in the final or decay section:

Is this ⌐my ⌐coat?⟋

The primary stress in this question is placed on *my* and the last direction of pitch change in the final section is rising, as indicated by the question in this instance. A melody pattern for any language would be constructed of a sufficient number of such intonation phrases linked together by pauses or transitions of various types. Such an intonation complex would be sufficient to express an intended idea in the native language of the speaker.

Just as every language has its individual set of sounds, every language has its characteristic intonation patterns varying in the same characteristics of form and distribution. Each are used by the speaker to satisfy the demands of the communication situation. Comparison of foreign intonation patterns with those of a comparable native American English speaker expressing the same ideas will permit the therapist to recognize the points at which the two patterns of intonation are similar and different.

The Japanese student frequently says,

You ⌐like?⟋

with rising intonation. The American English speaker may also say,

Do you ⌐like it?⟋

If he desires an answer, he may also say,

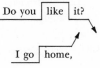

Do you ⌐like ⌐it?⟍

The Russian says,

I go ⌐home,⟍

while the American English speaker states his intention in the sentence,

I ⌐will go hǒme.⟍

The scientific information available at present for the study of intonation patterns is not as extensive as that found in the investigation of phonemes or of individual sounds of language. Future research will assist the clinician or teacher in this phase of foreign-accent therapy as it has in other areas of second-language learning. Until such time as the results of research are available, the therapist must prepare his own materials for evaluating student abilities in intonation and melody of American English speech.

> 28   Most speech-correction texts have sections devoted to testing of pitch
> disorders. Fairbanks (36:122-34) and Anderson (3) offer sections on
> evaluation of pitch in vocal expression. Lado (85:117-40) explains meth-
> ods of constructing a test of pitch discrimination for foreign students.

INTONATION AND MELODY PROBLEMS

As you listen to the speech of the second-language learner, your first impression of foreign accent is derived from the stream of speech. *Pitch* variations appear in unnatural places or the presence of a monotonous pitch level is detected. The *loudness* of the sound in the essential places in English is absent. *Length* of sounds and pauses have been rearranged so that misplaced variation in sound-silence patterns can be detected. Finally, the *quality* of sound is changed.

> 29   The label *foreign accent* is applied to a speech pattern by the listener
> on the basis of the way he hears the sounds of the talker in terms of
> his own speech background. Miller (104:47-79) and Fry (46:169-73)
> present psychological and physical characteristics of heard speech as
> they relate to the production of that speech.

These four sound features of melody in speech—*pitch, loudness, length,* sometimes called *duration,* and *quality*—are considered the prosodic elements of language and are fundamental dimensions in differentiating one language from another. Research appears to confirm that the phonemes of speech in two languages are also differentiated on the basis of these elements. Pitch variation forms the foundation for the intonation phrase discussed earlier, but it cannot be divorced from the other three factors except for purposes of explanation and illustration.

In American English the intonation phrases used by the speaker have certain communicative or emotional significance designated according to the *form* in which they are structured and spoken and according to the *distribution* in the flow pattern of a spoken communication. In English, the intonation phrase consists of an approach pitch, either an inflection or a step, a center of pitch and emphasis, and a decay phase in which the pitch is once more inflected or an abrupt silence which concludes the idea as a pause accompanied by silence of varying duration.

The intonation pattern of English is a product of psychological adjustment of the speaker to the speech situation, as well as the physical characteristics of the sound produced. The speaker may acquire all of the necessary mechanical and physical features contained in speech and yet the utterance may be lacking in essential communicative value for the native listener. Mechanically produced speech has this characteristic at present. Pitch control is one essential in the production of language intonation patterns acquired in childhood by the native speaker. It *must be taught* for a second language in terms of the needs of that language.

TONE LANGUAGE AND INTONATION

It is important to differentiate between *tone* used in reference to the general quality of voice used by the speaker and the use of the word in reference to *tone languages*. This is significant because the students who have spoken tone languages such as Chinese, Burmese, Indo-Chinese, or a number of Oriental languages, one of the western or southern African languages called *tone languages,* or one of the various Indian languages of North or South America, will have difficulty understanding the explanation of intonation used in the classroom and the clinic. If the native language of the student has been a *tone language,* the lexical use of tone to differentiate distinctive meanings in their language will complicate their use of intonation and melody in American English.

> Are you interested in reading about tone languages? Heffner (62) introduces the subject in his discussion of pitch, intonation, and melody. He considers the term *tone language,* "not altogether a happy one since no language can be devoid of tone...." Burssens (18:330-35) summarizes the use of tone in African tone languages.

In Mandarin Chinese there are four tones which function to give lexical significance to the same group of sounds used as a word or group of words. Perhaps the best way to understand the system would be to contrast the use of pitch change in Chinese with that in American English. Teng Ssu-yu (*137*:2-9) gives the following example of the tones of Chinese. Imagine that you are applying the same tones to the following English expressions. The four tones in Chinese are comparable to the following:

> First tone—slight surprise—Oh.
> Second tone—question————Oh?
> Third tone—doubt——————O-oh?
> Fourth tone—emphasis———Oh!

In the same way the change of tone in Chinese will change the meaning of the sounds produced lexically instead of by implication as it does in English. Thus, the sound combinations used in various tones will give the following meaning to the same combination of phonemes [ma] produced by the Chinese speaker:

> First tone—somewhat high, level, slightly prolonged—means *mother.*
> Second tone—a rising tone—means *hemp.*
> Third tone—starts moderately high, drops rather low, and then rises slightly at the end—means *yard.*
> Fourth tone—brief, comes to a full stop, like the end of a sentence— means *to scold.*

Such a contrast between the use of pitch changes in American English and those used in Chinese or in any other tone language emphasizes that correct tones are indispensable in such a language. The flexibility allowed in the use of pitch within English intonation and melody patterns will be confusing to the student whose native language is Chinese.

In African language, as in many other tone languages, the intervals between the notes are the important delineating characteristics for giving meaning. Such tones may differ in height or in direction when functioning as marks of distinctive meaning. When tone is used for this purpose, there are two applications in a language. First, the pitch may be employed to *indicate meaning,* called in our previous discussion of Chinese *lexical tones.* Second, pitch may be used to *indicate grammatical relationships* in meaningful patterns. Such tones are called *grammatical tones.* Burssens (*18*:330-35) presents fourteen meanings that can be given to a group of words, in sentence form, in Tshiluba, a dialect of Bantu from the Belgian Congo, by varying the lexical or grammatical tones on the unchanged phonemes. He cites the following example: "múfɔ̀ ùdí mú diùlú" means "The Lord is in heaven"; while "múlɔ́fɔ̀ ùdí mù diùlù" means "The Lord is there, Diulu" (a village). Contrasts in tones are indicated by markings above letters.

American English also utilizes change of pitch for the purpose of changing meaning, but this process is not parallel to the change in a tone language since the referent remains the same. The question is asked: You don't like it? The same words are used for the statement, but change of pitch indicates the difference: You don't like it. American English uses this method of varying pitch or intonation pattern to change meaning. It is called a *prosodic feature* of the language by some writers. In a tone language not only does the implication change with a change in pitch, but the referent also is shifted with a change of tone.

When the number of tone patterns change from the four of our Chinese example to the dozen or more used in the Bantu dialect just described, it can be understood why certain African students have problems with the intonation of American English.

A third group is languages which are similar in general to English in intonation pattern but have a few characteristic forms in which the use of tones separates the meanings of the words. Two of these languages are Swedish and Norwegian. In Norwegian and Swedish the use of tone, although limited, does appear in differentiating meaning. There are two tones used in the Oslo dialect. Heffner (62) illustrates these two tones as differentiating between the words "*gassen,* 'the gas,' *anden,* 'the duck,' *jernet,* 'the iron,' and *skallet,* 'the shell,' " when the first tone is used and "*gassen,* 'the gander,' *anden,* 'the second,' *gjerne,* 'gladly' and *skolle,* 'skull,' " when the second tone is used to make the difference in intonation pattern. Minor differences in spelling of several words do not alter the pronunciation situation as *gjerne* and *jernet,* as well as *skolle* and *skallet* are produced with the same sounds, the only difference being in the tone.

> 31   The integrative behavior of language learning is at the basis of speech interference. Vigotsky (146) discusses speech as it relates to inner language and the meaning of such language to the psychology of language and thought.

If the student moves from one *tone language* to another as is the case in Chinese dialects, American Indian dialects, or African tone languages, the ability to use "tone" will provide some facility in second-language learning. When the second language is "nontone" as far as meaningful structure is concerned, our student will carry over his habits of tonal use to his disadvantage. This will be the problem in learning to speak American English. English spoken with the accepted tones of Mandarin Chinese, Tshiluba, or Oslo Norwegian may be perfectly pronounced phonetically and grammatically exact, but the speech may still have a marked foreign accent to the native American listener. Unless the intonation reflects the English melody rather than the melody native to the Chinese, African, or Nordic tongues, the speaker will be heard as speaking with a *foreign accent.* *Tone* and *intonation* signify different ways of utilizing pitch change in the languages of the world and the clinician's knowledge of each system will assist him in understanding this speech problem.

THERE ARE THOSE WHO CONTEND THAT RHYTHM IS A PART OF A UNIVERsal law made manifest in all organic and inorganic matter. This cyclic movement or fluctuation marked by regular recurrence is said to be exhibited in the heartbeat, in the circulatory system, in sexual activities, in respiration, and in hundreds of other time patterns of living organisms. The diurnal character of life with its nights and days, its change of seasons, and the rising and setting of the sun and moon underline the rhythmic characteristics of the inorganic world. Electrons and planets alike whirl in their orbits.

Speech, the product of respiration and the coordinated action of the vocal folds, carries patterned recurrences of sound and silence

5 *patterns of stress and rhythm*

in a manner which makes rhythm a basic component of all speech. Each language has a characteristic rhythm revealed in the relationships of stressed and unstressed syllables contrasting with each other and with periods of silence of different duration. Stress is not only a measure of intensity or loudness in sounds produced; experiments have shown that stress perception is also a result of the operation of such features as vowel color and duration of sound. These are as important as intensity or loudness in determining the stress characteristics of a language. Stress may be of several varieties, each being

32   Stress has been investigated experimentally as well as logically. Fry (46:169-73) summarizes the results of experimental evidence in perception of stress. Newman (112:171-87) classifies the "stress accents" and contrasts them with the "expressive accents."

utilized in the same language to change the meaning of words individually or in context.

The regular recurrence of stressed syllables interspersed with periods of silence of varying lengths adds rhythmic patterning to an utterance. These two factors are illustrated by the sentence:

$$\text{Where are you} \quad \text{going} \quad | \; | \quad \text{in such a} \quad \text{hurry?}$$

THE SYLLABLE

As the flow pattern of speech is analyzed into its components, the most frequently mentioned unit in the literature, whether the writing is in experimental phonetics, linguistics, poetry, or polyphonic prose, is the *syllable*. In a manner similar to many of the other terms used in speech and language study, there is no unanimous agreement, at present, on the character and function of the syllable. Just

> 33 Stetson (133) defines the "syllable pulse" with which he explains his motor phonetic theory. Carrell and Tiffany (21) use the syllable as a contrast with the individual speech sound in comparing stress and rhythm in speech.

as the intonation phrase may be said to possess features which can be identified as an approach phase, a peak, and a period of decay or "terminal contour," the syllable can also be subdivided into three or four parts, each with its own boundaries and characteristics. Each language has some characteristic contrasts with American English in the way its syllables are employed to provide for stress in speech. These uses are widely divergent. Germanic language uses stress in similar ways, but the location of the stress element in a flow of words differs with each individual tongue. You may remember the old rules in German: stress falls on the stem syllable, usually on the negative prefix *un* and its associated forms *im* and *in*, on the suffix *ei*, as well as on the first component of a compound word. Finally, inseparable prefixes are never accented. In this very compact set of rules most of the basic stress characteristics for German are summarized. Unfortunately for the foreign student, American English has no such concise directives for its stress. The German student carries over his habit of stressing the first syllable in such words as *unknown, unprepared,* and *unfair;* American English places the primary stress on the second syllable.

The Spanish student has learned the rules of Spanish accent which say: (*a*) if the word ends in a consonant (except *n* or *s*) stress the last syllable, (*b*) if the word ends in a vowel, *n* or *s*, stress the next-to-the-last syllable, and (*c*) all words not pronounced according to the above rules must have a written accent, ('). In such words as *com-plexion, constitution,* and *combination* the differing patterns of stress in English are added to the difference in syllabification in the two languages, thus causing the Spanish student to speak with a foreign accent because he misplaces the stress when speaking English. He says [kom plek θi'on], [kon sti tuθi'on], and [kom bi neθi'on], using the accentual pattern from Spanish even though there is no printed accent mark in English.

According to some authorities, French has no stress pattern which is phonemic in character. However, it does use an expressive stress which is subtly fused with the intonation pattern and most difficult for the English ear to detect. When the native French speaker attempts to produce the various phonemic stresses in such American English words as *literature* and *delimitation,* these words become *literature* and *delimitation,* because he carries over his native accents from the French cognates.

Certain dialects of Chinese and Vietnamese are among the languages that use tone as the accentual system rather than stress, defined as intensity or loudness. Some tone languages have as many as eight or nine tones used for phonemic or expressive purposes. When the method of giving prominence to syllables, words, and phrases is by contrast of loudness or intensity, change in "tone" or pitch variation, or distribution of sound and silence, each language uses a method peculiar to the speech of that tongue.

There has been some controversy as to whether the syllable, as a unit of sound, or an individual sound within the syllable is the recipient of stress in language. For purposes of our discussion, we will assume that the syllable is the receiver of the stress force and that rhythm is produced by patterns of alternately stressed and unstressed syllables.

A syllable in American English is a unit of spoken language consisting of a vowel [u], *a diphthong* [ɑɪ], *or a syllabic consonant* [l] *as in cattle* [kætl], *alone or in combination with one or more consonants preceding or following in the sound group.* Parts of the syllable have been named the *onset,* the *peak,* and the *coda.*

In terms of physiological production, the names *hypha* and *syllable pulse* have been assigned to the stress features of the syllable. The initial boundary of the hypha is described by Meader and Muyskens (*99*:29-30) as "the beginning of a movement reducing the degree of closure of the passage which has resulted from a preceding constriction or occlusion. Its terminal boundary is the conclusion of a movement of constriction or occlusion." Such an action in speech is regarded as a *physiological syllable* and the word *act* is used to illustrate the action in a voiceless hypha between the sounds [k] and [t] in [ækt]. The continuous sound of the [æ] is broken by the occlusion for [k]. When the constriction is broken the hypha begins and continues until the next occlusion or maximum constriction is complete. Thus, the hypha might be considered the syllable boundary. Similarly, the syllable pulse is regarded as chest pulse released and arrested by muscular action and containing a vowel peak. In such a syllable as [bɪb], the initial [b] and the final [b] will differ in physiological character.

American English uses the stress system in which the major emphasis within the syllable is on the vowel. Called a *peak system,* such a method of stress contrasts with patterns of syllable stress used in other languages. French students frequently contend that American English students "always say things so positively." They are always "emphasizing all of the words." In reality, the English speaker does not emphasize all of the words but distributes his stress points in a pattern of *uniform time.*

When phrases, clauses, and sentences are spoken in English, it is possible to hear a fairly uniform length of time between major stress points, regardless of the number of syllables included in the sound space between primary stresses. This contrasts with certain Romance languages, notably Spanish and sometimes French, as well as with German and Japanese, in which the syllables are presented as individually spaced units. Thus, the sentence is as long as the number of syllables it contains. The English habit of telescoping syllable stresses for rhythmic purposes is missing in these languages. When the speaker of German, Japanese, or Spanish transfers his syllable stress and rhythm patterns into English, the native listener hears the syllables between each primary stress given equal emphasis in "overemphasized" speech and sound. This contrasts with American English in which certain syllables are usually reduced in importance through lack of stress.

In the sentence, Thís is the bróther of my friénd, the maximum peaks are marked for the average American English speaker. Note that the syllables between each major peak are reduced in stress quantity. When the speaker whose native language is one of the Romance groups (French, Spanish, Italian), his use of individual syllabic stress would frequently sound as though he were saying, Thís ís the bróther óf my friénd. Such a stress pattern on individual syllable associated with the lack of the characteristic "unstressing" so common in American English creates an abnormal speech rhythm as well as a lack of primary stress points. Distortion of stress and rhythm will frequently be a contributing factor in foreign accent.

34   Recognition of syllables and the stress patterns used in accentuating syllables is best known in the study of poetry. Sarett, Foster, and Sarett (124:276-309) define stress and rhythm and offer exercises for developing an appreciation of various types of rhythm. Slager and his associates (130) provide drills of stress in isolated words and connected speech in each of the texts of the *English for Today Series.*

STRESS IN AMERICAN ENGLISH

In most modern languages, stress may be a phonemic feature when it is used to distinguish between words having the same phonetic sound structures in the language. For example, the words *increase* and *increase* are both composed of the same phonetic sounds. They look the same when written, but if we place the stress on the first of the two syllables, the word becomes a noun form and may be used in a substantive position in the sentence. If the stress is placed on the second syllable of the word, the form and function of the word changes, even though it is still composed of the same sounds. In the example, I want an increase in my salary, the word is used as a noun and the stress signals that intention, as well as the context in which it is used. The boss may respond, I can't incréase your salary at this time. You may decide to look elsewhere for employment, but you will also know that the boss was using a verb form in spite of the context. The same change appears in such words as *object,* in I objéct to that hat, or That hat is not the óbject of my approval. Some authorities would say that there is a change in the phonetic values of the two initial sounds as well as in the stress. Thus, the sound cue which signals the difference is not one of stress alone but of stress and phoneme combined. This occurs frequently in English and adds to the confusion of the foreign student.

CHARACTERISTIC STRESS IN FOREIGN ACCENT

Let us assume that the syllable is a basic unit of American English speech and that it receives stress of varying degrees for the purpose of giving meaning. As we listen to the hum of conversation in the lecture hall or in the student union, we recognize that there are varieties of emphasis in English which distinguish the rhythm patterns of our language from the stress patterns of other languages.

The ways in which stress may be used are infinite, but there are only three important ways in which American English stress patterns create problems for the second-language learner. First, stress may be used as a "phonemic" factor in English. Second, stress is employed to give "expressive accent" to the words of an utterance. Third, when stress in the form of de-emphasis is used in American English, the term *unstressing* is applied to the resulting speech characteristic.

STRESS AS A PHONEME

When stress functions in a phonemic capacity as one of the segmental phonemes, word differences may depend upon accent features alone. A classic example of this function used in the literature in the word combination, *blackbird,* a species of bird, and *black bird,* any bird colored black. The difference between these two words will depend upon stress or upon a combination of stress and pause interval between the two words. Many people will omit the interval and make the difference by varying the stress pattern; others will produce two different types of stress on the second syllable or on the second word of the series.

Two major classification systems have been devised by students of stress; accent and emphasis. Each system has variations in application, and different titles are used to designate the classes of stress used phonemically. Both the three-stress system and the four-stress system are applicable in teaching English as a second language. It would seem advisable for the clinician and teacher to use a three-

35   Prator (119:16-8), Fairbanks (36:159-69), and Leutenegger (94:135-36) recommend the three-stress system. Bronstein (14:247-48) describes both systems as they are used in the pronunciation of American English.

division system in working with students who are learning English for the first time, since the gradation of differences is much larger than it is in a four-step system. The four-step system is presented as *primary, secondary, tertiary,* and *weak.* Variations of these names are found in the literature as follows: *strong* or *strong-loud* for primary; *loud, intermediate,* or *medium* for secondary; *weak-loud* for tertiary; and *unstressed* or *unaccented* for weak. Choose your own system of titles for the various classifications of stress but be consistent as you build your program.

The three-class division of stress omits tertiary, leaving primary as the most prominent syllable in the complex and secondary as the amount of stress between the strong pulse of primary and the lack of stress commonly classified as weak. These three modes of stress will be recognized in our discussion; two of them will be marked with symbols (′) and (‚). The symbol for primary stress will be written above the line and before the syllable receiving the primary stress in a word. Secondary stress will be designated by the (‚) symbol and will be written below the line and before the syllable receiving the secondary stress. Other syllables of the word will remain unmarked.

36   Dictionaries as well as writers use a variety of notation systems for indicating word accents. The system used in this text is employed by Kenyon and Knott (81:xxiv-xxvi).

In testing the phonemic stress patterns of the student, two types of tests should be devised: one test should be for *hearing* and *recognizing* the differences between primary, secondary, and weak stresses within words of both single and compound forms; the other should evaluate the student's ability to *produce* these same stress patterns as they are heard or associated with the marking system selected by the clinician or teacher.

37   Help may be obtained in building such tests from Lado (85:105-15) and Prator (119:23-36).

Since all languages are characterized by some form of contrast in the stream of speech, we can assume that our students will recognize basic loudness differences in the flow of sound; however, we cannot conclude that they will use these differences phonemically as they are used in American English. By knowing the language background of the student and the ways in which loudness, pitch, rhythm, and duration are used for contrast in the native language, the teacher or clinician is able to compare systems of stress in the native and second languages. Such a comparison of distinctive elements should provide a basis for objective attack on the stress features of foreign accent.

Sentence sense or sense stress

When the speaker produces more than a single word in an utterance, the pattern of stress and rhythm may change to meet this changing oral situation. As you look at this printed page, the words are all neatly arranged with space between each word symbol. Read aloud the first paragraph and you will discover that the spaces between the words disappear and words, all printed in the same shade of gray or black, take on varying intensities in sound that have not been reproduced on the printed page. This difference in sound cannot be reproduced in a dictionary, even a pronouncing dictionary, for each word in every context of English. Unlike some other languages in which words retain their individual stress, intonation, and duration patterns in context as well as in isolation, English uses prosodic features of language to change meaning in context. Stress may, therefore, be used in this manner.

The drill familiar to students of speech and drama may serve to illustrate the principle of rhetorical use of stress. The drill sentence used usually consists of four or five words such as: *This is my seat.* Each student is asked to change the meaning of the sentence by changing the "sense stress." Such a problem in American English might result in:

This is my seat.   (Not the one in which you are sitting.)

This is my seat.   (Though you have denied it, I contend it is true.)

This is my seat.   (It is not your seat, it is mine.)

This is my seat.   (Not the place to stand but the seat.)

It is not practical to list all the possibilities of variation in sound characteristics used in English to express ideas with stress or accent. Perhaps someday research laboratories will be able to classify and describe the individual forms of expressive stress. Until that time we will need to generalize about the features and teach our students the methods of sentence stress used in American English from a pragmatic point of view.

In order to establish "expressive accent" in a series of words, the sense stress of the various words is frequently associated with other prosodic features. The word may be raised in pitch to add a feature of incredulity or questioning as in the sentence:

This is my seat? (Do you mean that you are asking me to sit in *that* seat?)

The pause may also precede the word *my* to emphasize the ridiculousness of the situation. Further emphasis might be obtained by reducing the *quantity* of the first two words before the pause. Such a verbal action might reduce the initial sound of *is* to [ə], resulting in the statement sounding like [ðɪs əz mɑɪː sit]

It is possible to see the variety of sound characteristics which co-operate to make expressive accent function in American English. These characteristics all relate to stress. We cannot divorce meaning in English from stress and its related acoustic characteristics.

> 38 Meaning, one characteristic of every language, is conveyed by vocal expression. Sarett, Foster, and Sarett (124:276-309) relate meaning to the voice elements. Smith and Linn (131:115-64) discuss the conversion of the written word into oral expression in terms of expressive accent.

PROBLEMS OF STRESS—BUILDING FOUNDATIONS

Since the rhythm patterns of life are all about us, illustrations should be easily found in the modern music so popular with students of all ages. Discussion and listening might begin with the following exercises. A drum, tom-tom, block of wood, drumstick, or merely a hand on the book or desk may be used to illustrate the patterns.*

1. Gross Accent

Begin this basic training with single individual beats. Illustrate a loud beat and a soft beat, a short beat and a long beat, alternating short and long beats. Each pattern should be produced by the student or students learning the language. This repetition can be done after demonstration by the instructor, but patterns produced simultaneously emphasize the simultaneous listening. Use both familiar and unfamiliar beat patterns to free the foreign students from the basic beats of their own language's cultural and structural patterns. These beats should be produced simultaneously by the instructor and students so that strong visual and kinesthetic feedbacks will reinforce the auditory impressions. The head should be moved in rhythm or jerked, the body should sway, and the arms, legs, and feet should be used to keep time. Even more important, once the body has found the beat, the breathing should be brought into synchrony. Patterns of inhalatory gasps and expiratory breath pulses can be

---

* In the exercises of stress the (——) will be used to illustrate the loud beat, a (══) will indicate an extra-loud beat, and (⌣) will signify a less-loud beat which is shorter in length. These symbols are used rather than the accent notations to simplify instructions for the beginner. Regular notation symbols for accent could be used in conjunction with the patterns as soon as the student has learned to produce the necessary variations in stress.

blended into the gross motor activity. Grunts, speech sounds, and nonsense syllables can implement the rhythms. The teacher must serve as the conductor of a new orchestra, building a sense of time and rhythm in his performers. Often this basic training proceeds swiftly and the basic patterns of stress in English grow out of the bodily activity. They may be chanted, at first, then spoken as control of gross stress patterns is attained.

2. Patterns of Stress

In preparation for practicing word accents use one major strong beat (——). After the student is capable of producing a single beat with precision, associate the beat with a word containing a single stress peak.

<u>name</u>   <u>hand</u>   <u>coat</u>

Utilize vocabulary words suitable for the appropriate level of instruction.

a. Words of two syllables may next be used. Such patterns should include words such as the days of the week, since they are essential early in learning English.

<u>Monday</u>   <u>Tuesday</u>   <u>Wednesday</u>

Some instructors may prefer to move directly to the use of single-syllable words in phrase and sentence contexts in order to fully develop the single strong stress before moving to a contrast.

b. Polysyllabic words can be used with students who have had previous experience with English. Words of two syllables are sufficient for this practice. Word lists in Slager (*130*) are useful in this drill because they have been graded in difficulty. Students with varying language backgrounds will have differing degrees of difficulty in stress practice. French, Persian, and Indian students may have difficulty in producing contrasts in "beat." Spanish and Italian students will be able to produce the emphatic beat but will tend to compress pauses between the beats into regular intervals. German and Hungarian students experience little difficulty, but for them contrasts in loudness may be difficult to learn. Words which have immediate utilitarian value in the class should be introduced. Some of these are: altogether, anyone, attention, auditorium, beginning, celebration, ceremony, certificate, and so forth.

3. Sense Stress

Having established contrasts in loud and soft beats and long and short beats with varying intervals between them, the student will need assistance in associating these patterns. Patterned practice statements in conversation can be used for the beginner and formal speaking and reading can be used for more advanced second-language students. Again, echo speech or shadowing are useful here.

a. Single beats in series provide a good beginning. The instructor produces four or five equally loud beats having approximately the same length for imitation by the student. The number selected might be the same as the number of monosyllabic words to be used in the first drill sentences.

⎯⎯⎯⎯   ⎯⎯⎯⎯   ⎯⎯⎯⎯   ⎯⎯⎯⎯   ⎯⎯⎯⎯

You may find that some students experience difficulty repeating even these simple, regular, rhythm patterns; if so, more basic training is required.

b. To test retention, simultaneous reproduction practice may be followed by imitative practice, inserting increased delays between production by the instructor and reproduction by the student. Our task is to create internal and covert models. We must free the student from his dependence upon our stimulation. His auditory memory span must be trained for accents heard and reproduced. Often during the delay between stimulation and reproduction the student should rehearse, first in a whisper, then in pantomime, then in such motor activities as breath pulse, finger tapping or head gesturing, the basic beat patterns of the speech he has just heard. This silent incorporation of the model allows it to serve as an internal monitor for his own reproduction.

Patterns of sense stress may be taught by having the student beat out a rhythm of his native language. After testing various patterns of rhythm, compare these with the rhythms of American English. Discussion of the points of contrast and similarity will be of assistance to the learner.

39   Practice in stress patterns will be found in Gordon and Wong (48:19-44), Prator (119:23-36), and Fairbanks (36:155-69). Fries (44) provides the most thorough second-language program for Spanish-speaking students.

c. Having established the ability to reproduce the pattern of regular beats with the instructor and in imitation after a pause, the student is next asked to vary the pattern in loudness on the five beats: strong beat at the start followed by four lighter beats.

d. Words can be associated with the patterns of rhythm to fit the meaning.

This is my new coat.

This is my new coat.

e. Variation of pattern in order to emphasize two or more words using the "stress timed" rhythms of American English can be used to amplify the content of the material.

This is my new coat.

This is my new coat.

f. Changes in length of the subordinate beats in the sentence to clarify the time-stress patterns will assist the student in developing natural American English rhythms.

This is my new coat.

This is my new coat.

> 40 Stress on adjectives and nouns in American English has been a matter of controversy in speech. Bolinger (9:5-20) emphasizes the confusion in the areas of stress analysis in English.

TYPES OF EXPRESSIVE STRESS

Sentence stress may vary in two directions or the goal may be accomplished by two methods. First, sentence stress may be used to obtain emphasis by *intensity*. Second, the emphasis may be obtained by *contrast*.

When seeking to produce emphasis by intensity in American English, the speaker may obtain the stress by increasing the loudness of an already stressed vowel which is the peak of a syllable. For example, the sentence spoken might be:

The view of the Grand Canyon is magnificent.

A normal stress pattern of the sentence might emphasize the words view, Grand Canyon, and magnificent with the peak of the stress appearing on the second syllable of the word magnificent. To gain the desired intensity of utterance, the sentence might be read as:

The VIEW of the Grand Canyon was magNIFicent.

An emphasis on the second syllable would, in reality, distort the word by magnifying the stress comparison between one syllable, ordinarily strongly stressed, and the remaining syllables in the word and sentence. Such words as tremendous, extravagant, fabulous are frequently used to gain emphasis by intensity. The second-language learner repeatedly attempts to imitate the production of emphasis by intensity and misplaces the accent, placing it on the final syllable which creates a humorous situation rather than a heightened interest. The French speaker says fabulous, transferring his native accent from *fabuleux* or extravagant, using his experience with extravagance to give him the cue for the emphasis through intensity.

In American English, intensity may also be used for emphasis by shifting the stress to an unstressed vowel. This is used to create an effect of increased intensity and may be misunderstood by the speaker of another language. If we produce the following sentence in the normal fashion it is:

> I saw an enormous tidal wave.

With stress placed on an unstressed syllable the pattern becomes:

> I saw an E-NOR-mous tidal wave.

Unnatural as the pattern may sound, it is used regularly in modern American speech to obtain sense stress through increased intensity on the unstressed syllable. Such uses of stress which distort or change the normal phonemes of the word are misunderstood by the foreign student. Linked with their habitual tendency to produce the sound of the vowel as it would be produced without unstressing the word becomes [inərmas] instead of [ɪnɔrməs].

Second, the use of emphasis by contrast is developed through increase of stress on one word and reducing the stress on related words in the sentence. Try saying the words "I am here" in as many ways as possible. You will note that as the configuration of stress is changed from

> I am here   to   I am here

the meaning has been changed, even though you may control the change in pitch and the length or quantity of the vowel.

> My name is ———.
> My name is ———.
> My name is ———.

Such practice can be introduced using the drum or tom-tom to produce beats.

Two contrast words may be used in the same sentence to produce comparisons of stress for developing sentence sense. Such sentences as:

> This book is mine.
> That book is yours.
> The S.U.B. is on the corner.

Similarly, the peaks in a sentence can be increased to three in order to establish the time-space rhythm patterns that are customary in American English speech.

> The book on the small table is mine.
> The blue book in the desk belongs to you.
> The three-story building on the corner is called the S.U.B.

Stress can also be made more evident by producing direct contrasts between sound and silence. When the word to be emphasized is set off by pauses of varying lengths, before and after the unit of sound, it is emphasized by this contrast.

> I will || not || go.

> Give me a || large || glass of milk.

Since stress is regarded as a matter of degrees of contrast rather than an absolute value in language, the silence heightens the emphatic nature of the word isolated even though the intensity level has not been raised above that of the remaining words of the statement.

UNSTRESSING IN AMERICAN ENGLISH

Among the difficulties encountered by students learning English speech is the acquisition of that characteristic sound feature of language called *unstressing*. Defined as the *"lightest stress found in language short of zero"* stress, this opposition to force or intensity, is present in all dialects of American English. The tendency to de-emphasize the vowel stresses in certain settings, which originated in primitive Indo-European, passed through the Germanic tongues and into Old, Middle, and Modern English and has reached its most prevalent use in modern American English.

41　　Unstressing has historical and modern functional associations. Kenyon
(80:87-110) reviews the tendency for vowels in unaccented positions to
become obscure.

In English, when vowels are stressed, they are produced with "full phonetic value." When syllables are unstressed, the same vowels become [ə], [ɪ], or [ɪ] or [ʊ], depending upon the method of transcribing the central vowels. This process of reducing stress frequently leads to the shortening of vowel length or *quantity*. For example: This is my Uncle Jim [ðɪs ɪz maɪ ʌŋkl̩ dʒɪm] becomes [ðɪz əz məŋkl̩ dʒɪm]. Also accompanying the process may be a reduction in pitch and a change in vowel resonance. Unstressing affects all of the prosodic features of speech so that a total change is created in the sound pattern of the word, phrase, or sentence.

Unstressing is a central feature of American speech and *must be learned* by the student who wishes to speak our language without a foreign accent. Accustomed to precise syllable-spaced articulation or the complete lack of peak syllable stress, he will need help in unstressing. Students of French, Persian, and American Indian language origins will have difficulty adjusting to the time-spaced rhythm of American English as they attempt to use any unstressed vowels in the proper positions. Speakers whose languages include German, Hungarian, Spanish, Italian, Japanese, and Greek will face the need to reduce their precise articulation of each syllable by adopting the American English habit of "unstressing" if they are to speak without a foreign accent. This is our language. It differs in this regard from others.

PRACTICE IN STRESS CONTRASTS

Sense stress brings the essence of poetry and prose into speech. It is possible to introduce the sound feature called "unstressing" through stress patterns found in some poetic rhythms. Begin with the *iambic* pattern (‿ —) as produced on the percussion instrument. After the student has been taught to recognize the rhythm pattern and can produce it in imitation and independently in various sequences of one, two, or more repetitions, begin using the pattern with words. Use single words:

about　　　　　　upon　　　　　around　　　　　　unknown
‿ —　　　　　　‿ —　　　　　‿ —　　　　　　‿ —

Select nouns plus an article since students learning English have much difficulty with *a* and *the* in speech.

a chair	a door	a table	a book
‿ ‒	‿ ‒	‿ ‒	‿ ‒
the chair	the door	the table	the book

Such patterns must become automatic in rhythm as well as in sound production since one of the significant features of foreign accent is the tendency to place a stressed vowel in the article position. Thus, the speaker says [e ˈʃɛr] for the unstressed American English [ə ˈʃɛr]. Associating the rhythm with the sound production facilitates the acquisition of the unstressing or centralizing habit of American English for most students.

Another problem occurs when we come to longer utterances such as the prepositional phrases which show the rhythm (‿ ‿ ‒). The following examples indicate the rhythm pattern in metric form.*

on the chair	for the boy	in the box
‿ ‿ ‒	‿ ‿ ‒	‿ ‿ ‒

Each phrase can be varied in word substantive or object in order to practice the phrase stress in patterned drill. Thus, the list may be extended to include all the vocabulary words as they are introduced, being careful to use only one-syllable words at the beginning of patterned practice. Two-syllable words and polysyllabic forms should be introduced in separate sequences.

on the chair	for the boy	in the box
table	girl	house
shelf	man	bag
stove	dog	hole
bench	horse	shoe

Extension of this pattern to the full sentence might give a metric stress resembling the following sentences:

Here's a book on the desk. (‿ ‿ ‒ ‿ ‿ ‒)
There's a boy in the room. (‿ ‿ ‒ ‿ ‿ ‒)
Where's the lid for the box? (‿ ‿ ‒ ‿ ‿ ‒)

* It should be noted that the patterns suggested for practice are not consistent in English speech. They are the usual patterns of stress used in context but may be changed by the speaker who wishes to suggest meanings other than those commonly conveyed in the word combinations. Variety in intonation, pause, and length of sound are frequently used for the purpose of suggesting humor, sarcasm, or irony in American English. Attempts to suggest such implications will change the stress pattern when words are spoken in context.

Each sentence will require an intonation pattern in addition to the stress feature in order to give complete meaning. It should be possible to unite these two factors in patterned practice.

PAUSE AND RHYTHM IN FOREIGN ACCENT

Although a few languages contain sounds produced on inhalation —or sounds that are made without vibration of the vocal folds or by other parts of the vocal tract by exhaled air; it is the outgoing

42   Swedish *ja* ↓ and *jo* ↓, especially in women's speech, is produced on inhalation, according to Lotz (96:13-23). Jones (72) describes glottal stops and clicks used in languages of the world.

breath stream that produces the major speech force in all languages. The speaker pauses frequently to replenish the oxygen supply.

Languages differ in their use of pause. In English and in many other languages, the pause is used to allow the listener to "catch up" with the speaker, since auditory assimilation of ideas is somewhat slower than speech production. The pause may also be used to highlight a stress or intonation pattern used in the stress of speech. Frequently, the second language student will adopt the use of a

43   Smith and Linn (131:115-64) relate pause and "silences" to meaning in reading and speaking. Fairbanks (36:155-69) provides explanation and exercises for the use of pause in American English.

vocalized pause because his language does not make use of frequent pauses or complete silence in speech. For example, the Italian speaker says [ɑɪə gɑtə gretə lʌv fɔrə əmɛrikɑ]. Japanese and American Indian students have had difficulty acquiring the pause as a method of revealing sentence sense. Practice, using slash marks for pause indicators, assists readers to pause in the desirable places. For example, the single vertical or slant line (/) may be used to indicate a short pause and the double line, either vertical or slanting (//), may be used to indicate a longer pause. The use of such indicators might be demonstrated in the sentences:

Don't go.//You said you'd talk with me/and I have a question to ask.
It was a sunny day/with a slight breeze.
Do it right;//it must be exact.

In the illustrations, pauses of varying length are sometimes signalled by the punctuation, but in the first two sentences, the pauses are indicated by the sense of the sentence rather than by punctuation. It is this second type of pause that becomes most difficult because, to employ it, the foreign student must understand the meaning of the words and the implication of the idea. Ask the student to count the number of slash marks for the length of the pause; it facilitates the grasp of time lapse for pause. A series of steps in developing pause might be adopted. Counting aloud calls attention to the pause and the length. Counting to oneself gives an idea of length. Finally, allowing time to pass without the student's counting will allow the instructor to check the pauses. It is wise to have the student trace in the air with a forefinger the pause signals as the instructor is speaking. The natural rhythms of American English depend upon distribution of pause.

Significance of Pause

Within the sentence the pause relates the phrases and clauses to the central idea of the word group. Transitions of idea, especially in compound or complex sentences, are produced by pause plus the factors of intonation, stress, and duration of sound. In English the pause has several lengths, and each duration of pause carries meaning because it clusters groups of words or phrases and ties their meanings together into one idea.

Systematic study of the pauses in speech has not provided sufficient information to classify all pauses, but the *juncture* studies of the linguists assist us in working with this problem in foreign accent.

When you, as a native English speaker, hear the flow pattern of Italian, Arabic, or Spanish, you feel that the rate of speech is so rapid and the flow pattern so devoid of pause that you can never understand what is being said. The common complaint of students listening to native American English speech spoken at an average rate of 160 to 170 words per minute is that "Americans talk too fast." Our ears must become accustomed to the acoustic signals of the new language. Slowing the native rate of sound production and lengthening the normal pauses may make the spoken language easier to understand, but it does not assist the second-language learner because it distorts the pattern. The question:

What's your name?　Mine is Cal.

[wɑts jʊr nem　mɑɪn ɪz kæl]

is distorted if it is said:

[hw ɑt ɪz jʊɜr neɪm　mɑɪn ɪz kæl]

The length of a pause may be altered in context, just as the sounds within a word influence, and are influenced by, each other. In addition, the stress pattern will vary in intensity as different meanings are expressed.

Pause and Rhythm

Since pauses are the "punctuation marks of speech," they divide utterance into the meaningful units intended by the speaker. Distribution of pauses helps to cluster the words and phrases in order to develop relationship within word groups. When the metered recurrence of such moments of silence appears at regularly distributed intervals, rhythm evolves. Add to this pattern of recurring silences the word stresses plus the sentence sense beats and you have the essence of the rhythm of American English.

The distribution of syllables in time between stress points results in the stress-timed rhythms characteristic of English speech. If only

44   Languages and music rhythms have infinite variety and application as shown by De Groot (31:385-400).

a few syllables appear between these stress points the rate of speech may be slow, the sounds lengthened, and the pauses longer. If there are many syllables between pauses and stress points, the syllables are compressed into the time frame and the rate of speech is more rapid. Every language has an individual rhythm that is learned by the native speaker of that language before he is of school age. Like the intonation patterns and pitch changes used in the language, the features of intensity and emphasis are used by the infant and the maturing child to gain attention and to satisfy needs. Such habits are integrated into the native-language system.

People within a language group differ in their use of everyday speech rhythms. Some speak with regular, studied rhythms that use time and stress in a single pattern; others speak with rapid, choppy rhythm including many words and varied stress patterns within the time frame. Whatever the time-and-rhythm pattern may be, the speaker maintains an American English variation of stressed and unstressed syllables distributed in a basic pattern which is "typically English." If the nonnative speaker fails to acquire this pattern of stress and rhythm, he will be speaking with a foreign accent.

♩♩♩

IT IS NOT ESSENTIAL THAT A MAN BE BORN OUTSIDE THE AMERICAS, OR even outside the United States, to speak a non-English native language. Every year thousands of children are born within the states whose primary language will be something other than English. In urban New York, in the hills of Pennsylvania, in the Upper Peninsula of Michigan, along the bayous of Louisiana and Mississippi, in Chicago, in San Francisco, in Seattle, on the mesas and plains of New Mexico and Arizona, or beside the corrals of Texas, children are born and bathed to the sound of "foreign" speech. Spanish, French, Hungarian, Indian of a dozen different tongues, Chinese, Japanese, Polish and Russian, Finnish, and Hawaiian or other Ma-

6 *speech sounds and accent*

layan Polynesian are the native languages of the doctors, mid-wives and neighbors, the husbands, brothers and sisters who assist in delivering children.

Born on American soil but born in a native culture other than that of modern America, these children will learn the language of their brothers and sisters, the language of their parents. Whatever may be the advantages or disadvantages of such a sequence of language learning, the condition exists and the clinician will meet the polyglot in the clinic and classroom.

These children, regardless of their language background, will be thrown into an educational system that demands that they learn to speak English. If they escape the requirements of lawful school attendance, they will be seeking employment in an oral world where American English is the verbal coinage of communication. Many of these children, having been introduced to Cajun French, Pennsylvanian Dutch, New York Cuban Spanish, a pueblo Indian language, Gary Polish, or Chicago Italian, will be forced to learn English when they move out of their home environments or into the schools. The confusion in *sounds, speech structure,* and *speech meanings* which consist of layers of overlay from the languages to which the child has been exposed cause the polyglot condition.

Unlike the student who comes to the United States highly motivated and intent on learning American English as a second language, the *polyglot* often accepts his speech as "that's what God gave me." The problems of these people differ from those faced by the second-language learner from abroad.

SOUND PROBLEMS IN FOREIGN ACCENT

The search items and references of earlier chapters provide background for understanding the specific characteristics of General American phonology. Sagittal section diagrams and palatograms will not be used since they are available in general phonetics texts and linguistic texts.

> 45   You may find that visual aids are helpful in work with foreign accent. Kaplan (78) provides a review of basic anatomic principles for speech production. Kantner and West (77:141-86) offer the various palatograms and sagittal sections used in explaining the sounds of American English.

In this chapter our discussion of speech problems will be confined to those originating in the *absence* of American English sounds from the native language. Three representative examples of vowel problems and a similar number of consonant problems will be considered. In Chapter 5 the unstressing of American English sounds was presented as a part of the stress feature of American English. Associated with this practice is the sound unit [ə], sometimes called the *schwa*. According to Wise (*153*) the word is a German modification of the Hebrew word *scheva*. Some authorities consider the sound a variation of all sounds in the vowel pattern; others give it individual status.

The Schwa

The foreign student finds the [ə] one of the most difficult sounds of American English. Three attitudes toward this neutral sound have been assumed by writers in speech. First, the schwa may be regarded as an entity in itself, as in the words *upon* [əpɔn] and *above* [əbʌv]. This gives the sound phoneme status separate from [ʌ] in such nouns as *sun* [sʌn] and *tub* [tʌb]. The second group discusses the sound as an unstressed variety of the [ʌ] and as such merely an allophone of the phoneme. A third group looks upon [ə] as a sound "dumping ground caused by unstressing in each of the vowel phonemes." It is obvious that weak stress or unstressing is directly related to the [ə] and examples are found in American speech to illustrate that any vowel sound in the language may change to [ə].

46 Some speech sounds just defy special description! Wise (153) presents the unstressing point of view. Hubbell (68:105-11) and Coffee (27:103-9) discuss the problem from the phonetic point of view.

Whatever may be the philological, philosophical, or theoretical attitudes adopted by authorities in the speech area regarding the use of the [ə], the speech clinician and teacher working with foreign accent will encounter its production and use as a problem in learning American Speech.

The schwa is especially difficult for our foreign students because of its neutralness. Rules, the constant request of the second-language student, are lacking for application of the [ə] as used in American English.

The [ə] appears in the initial, medial, and final position of many word units in American speech. The four characteristics of defective articulation are evident in relation to this sound; a schwa sound is heard as an *addition* or *distortion,* an *omission,* and a *substitution* in foreign accent. It seems to obtrude everywhere, either by its inappropriate presence or by its significant absence. All those who work with foreign-flavored speech will find the schwa a prime focus of their work and instruction.

Addition of the sound appears in American English in the initial position as well as at the end of the word. As explained earlier, the foreign speaker has difficulty with the words of English beginning with *s.* Because Spanish words begin with an *e* before the *s,* the tendency is to carry over the habit into English, making the words *school, spend,* and *space* become [əskul], [əspɛnd], and [əspes]. Addition of the [ə] sound or some distortion of the phoneme is often heard when an attempt is made to produce the plosive final sounds used in American speech. When attempting to produce what the second-language learner hears as the final sound in such words as *bag* or *pod,* the speaker adds a voiced release which produces [bægə] and [padə]. The prominence of these initial and final additions becomes a vivid indicator of foreign accent.

Sound *substitutions* for the schwa are prevalent among second-language learners. In American English words that begin with *a* or *un,* such as *above* and *unknown*, the tendency is to produce [ɑnːnoʊn] and [ɑbɑv] for [ʌnːnoʊn] and [əbʌv]. In this pattern the student will frequently substitute the sound represented by the orthographic symbol in his native language. An example of such a substitution is [juniɔrm] for the American speech form [junəfɔrm] for the word *uniform* when used as either an adjective or a noun. A medial substitution also appears in the series of *dis* words, including *disability*, *disappear*, and *disappoint*, to name a few. The *a* usually sounded as an [ə] in American English becomes an [æ] sound if the student has acquired the sound. If he has not, the distortion of the sound may move up to [e] or down to [ɑ]. In either case, the sound substitution calls attention to the speaker's misuse of the [ə] sound.

For the students who learn their American English in the South or in the East, an added problem is presented in the form of the [r] plus the [ə]. The linking [r] is usually produced between vowels, but

47 The production of the [r] phoneme in American English has variety in
    medial and final positions when spoken in the various díalects of the
    language. Bronstein (14:116-23, 186-204) discusses the variations in
    terms of "r-less territory" of the United States.

in most other instances of vowel and [r] relationships, the [r] is omitted and the [ə] replaces the combination. Second-language learners have difficulty understanding the variable use of the schwa sound. Often, when attempting to produce the sound, the tendency is to "centralize" the vowels in words to such an extent that the entire speech pattern becomes "substandard" for the dialect area.

Distortion of the [ə] sound results when the speaker attempts to produce the neutral position of the vowel but fails to approximate the exact tongue position, cavity resonance, and lax condition. Such distortion may appear in the initial, medial or final position of a word. When the [ə] appears as many as two or three times in some common General American words such as laboratory [læbɚətɔrɪ], president [prɛzədənt], and communication [kəmjunəkəʃən], the distortion of each schwa sound produces bizarre sound effects [læbɔrætori], [prɛsidɛnt], and [komjunikeʃon].

The foreign student also has difficulty hearing the difference between the sounds [i] and [u] and the sounds [ɪ] and [ʊ] frequently used in American English when unstressing is present in the stream of speech. He may also have similar difficulty identifying the final sound in the words *variety* and *propriety*. When unstressed the sound is [ɪ], for example [vərɑɪəti] and [proprɑɪəti], but stressing the final syllable as some General American speakers do changes the final sound. In the medial position a similar situation evolves with the word *hear* [hɪɚ]. Of course the word *creek* has two pronunciations. One using the stressed [krik] and the other unstressed [krɪk] are both accepted in various dialects of American English. The production of the medial sound in *roof, root, poor,* and similar words serve as examples of the characteristic unstressing of the [u] among certain speakers. The student of a second language says, "If you can say [ruf] for [rʊf], why can't I say [luk] for [lʊk]?" The instructor may use his knowledge of distinctive differences and minimal pairs in English to explain the difference in phonemes, but the student will need to understand unstressing to appreciate the "neutralizing" of these sounds in American English.

The [æ] as in Cat

A second sound that creates problems for student speakers who have learned another language is the [æ] heard in the words *apple* [æpl̩], *pack* [pæk], and *bat* [bæt]. Norwegian and, to a very limited extent, Chinese are two of the few languages excluding English that use the sound [æ]. In the classroom and the clinic, the awkwardness of this sound will be called to the attention of the clinician by his second-language students. "I feel as though I'm showing all my teeth" has been heard in the laboratory. "It is such an uncomfortable sound to produce" was the comment of a dainty French student. Second-language learners have as much difficulty with the [æ] sound as the native English speaker has with the uvular or trilled *r,* the German [ç], and the nasalized sounds of French. To the native speaker of American English the [æ] is a simple sound, easily produced and poignantly expressive at times. For the nonnative learning to speak English, the production of the [æ] phoneme underlines his foreign accent.

Animal, apple, ashes, and such frequently used single syllable words as *an, at,* and *as* provide the [æ] sound in the initial position. The sound also appears in the medial and final position in single or multisyllable words but only rarely in the final position for such slang expressions or exclamations as [næ] or [bæ]. Sound distortions and sound substitutions are heard most regularly in this vowel. When the second-language student speaks, the additions of the sound appear only rarely as an overcompensation after learning the new sound production. Omissions of the sound are seldom heard when the second-language learner attempts to reproduce some companion sound for the vowel he hears spoken by the native American English speaker.

Common substitutions for the [æ] are the sounds [ε], [ə], and [ɑ], as well as distortions of these sounds in the medial positions. The [ε] and [ə] are substituted "because they hear native Americans use the sound" in such combinations as *an apple, am going,* and *as fast* when they are produced as [εn εpple], [əm goɪŋ], [əz fɑst] in rapid conversational speech. Although these productions are regarded as substandard in some areas, they are the forms frequently heard and used by the speaker of English as a second language.

Difficulty in producing the sound will be encountered by the student, especially if there is no similar allophone used in his native language. Three elements of the sound production can be emphasized. First, the mandible should be dropped and the tongue thrust forward until it touches the posterior surface of the lower dental arch. This tends to assist in contrasting the sounds [æ] and [ɑ]. Second, by keeping the tongue low and forward in the production of the sound, the tendency to nasalize the sound will be avoided. When the tongue becomes bunched at the rear of the oral cavity, there is an inclination to drop the velum and encourage nasal resonance, creating the hypernasal [æ] in *cat, last,* and *can,* [kæ̃t], [læ̃st], and [kæ̃n]. The sound may move as far as [ε] in similar words. Wise (204) contends that the [æ] sound differs from all the sounds above it on the vowel triangle "in the important feature that the lateral contact of the tongue with the upper teeth is definitely broken. It is the attempt to maintain this contact that produces the [æ] raised in the direction of [ε]." To avoid this movement the nonnative speaker should be taught to break the contact between the lateral portion of the tongue and the upper dental arch.

Once the student has acquired the ability to produce the [æ] sound in isolation, he will need contrast exercises with the sounds [ε], [ɑ], [ə], and [ʌ].

48   Leutenegger (94:54-57) explains the tense and lax allophones of this
      [ʌ] sound and provides drill exercises for practice.

The tendency to nasalize the [æ] sound in substandard American English speech discussed above provides an additional difficulty for the second-language student if he resides in an area where such a habit is prevalent. The native French speaker will rapidly adapt to this substandard sound pattern and assume that he is speaking "acceptable" American English speech.

Students in the clinic whose native language is Arabic produce the [ɑ] for the [æ] consistently in such words as *add, and, bat, dad, fatten, bath, catch, can, at,* and *rather.* This does not appear as a severe distortion or substitution in such words as *bath* and *can* as there are dialects of American English which use a similar sound in the words. It becomes confusing when contrasts in words *add/odd* and *damp/dump* are involved in such sentences as: I would add that it was an odd circumstance. Similarly, confusion would arise in a sentence such as: The house was located on the edge of a damp dump. Rare as the occasion might be in which such confusion would result, if there is a single instance of such contrast in a language the possibility of confusion exists.

Whenever the native language has allophones in the area of the [æ] phoneme, it creates difficulty for the English speech student in discriminating contrasts within minimal pairs such as bet/bat, cat/cut, bat/but, map/mop, sat/sought, and a variety of other similar contrasts involving the sounds [æ], [ɛ], [ɔ], [ɑ], and [ə] or [ʌ]. The single low-middle vowel of Arabic [ɑ] has allophones in this area, and sound substitutions or distortions are consistent when the [æ] sound is attempted.

> 49   The scientific study of the quality factor in vowels has provided significant information which may assist the clinician and teacher. Lentz and Sherman (93:381-98) and Peters (116:239-48) studied the dimensions of quality for the vowel [æ].

Because the [æ] is the most frequently accented sound spelled with the letter *a* in both British and American English, the speech student learning English of any dialect will have occasion to use the sound in conversation and business speech. When hearing these attempted sounds in the flow of conversational exchange or in the statements of informational speech, the native American English listener will catch the quality of foreign accent when the [æ] is improperly produced.

The [ʊ] *Used in Book*

Among the back vowels, the rounded, lax sound [ʊ] contrasts with the front, unrounded, lax vowel [æ] just discussed. Both sounds create difficulty for the speaker of American English as a second language. In such words as *took, look, full, pull, should,* and *would* the sound represents three combinations of written or printed letters. Because the sound appears only in the medial position in words that are of American English origin and very rarely in the initial position in such foreign-loan words as the German *umlaut,* which has been anglicized, the teaching of distribution of the [ʊ] is somewhat simplified. Only medial positions need to be used in the drill patterns, since the few foreign words employing the sound in the initial position may be taught individually in sentences as they would appear in English speech.

> 50   The [ʊ] has been classified with the [æ] as a "checked" vowel, as opposed to a "free" vowel, in the main Atlantic Seaboard System. Moulton (108) says some authorities regard the *checked* vowels as the only true vowels, since all *free* vowels can be classified as a vowel plus a consonant.

In any case, the [ʊ] sound is present in American English as a phoneme of all dialects. A similar phoneme is present in Roumanian, German, Hungarian, Finnish, and Norwegian. The majority of European languages have no [ʊ] and among those who have difficulty acquiring the sound in American English are the speakers of French, Italian, Spanish, Portuguese, Greek, Swedish, Danish, Russian, Polish, and Czech.

Such expressions as "He took my book" [hi tuk maɪ buk], or "The moon could put him in a good mood" [ðə mun kud put hɪm ɪn ə gud mud], demonstrate alternate substitutions. Substitutions and reversals are heard in the clinic or in the classroom when emphasis is placed on the [ʊ]. The most prevalent substitution for the [ʊ] is the [u] or a distortion of this sound for words having the double *o* spelling such as *book, look, took,* and *hook.* The student may move by analogy from the *soon* [sun] to *look* [luk], and from *moon* [mun] to *took* [tuk], when reading from the printed or written script. In those languages in which [ʊ] is an allophone of [u], the tendency to substitute follows the usual treatment of nondistinctive sounds in his native language.

Among polyglot individuals the tendency to change from [u] to [ʊ] is easily remedied in isolation, but teaching the consistent use of the sound in conversation and business speech requires more effort. Constant drills using the sound [ʌ] and [ʊ], as well as [ʊ] and [u] in minimal pairs of words in American English, will develop the habit when isolated production has been accomplished. Having established an ear for the contrast of the two sounds in isolated word units, the student could adapt the new sound to connected speech by patterned drill in sentences, dialogues, stories, and formal speech assignments.

Three vowels have been discussed briefly in relation to sound problems of the second-language learner when the vowel units of American English are encountered. Among the other vowels with which the nonnative student or polyglot student will have difficulty are the [ɛ], [ɔ], [ɝ], and [ʌ]. The comparison of the vowel structure of the native language with that of American English will indicate individual points of difference and possible areas of difficulty, but only a carefully analyzed recording with phonetic transcription will verify the areas of need in foreign accent.

DIPHTHONG PROBLEMS IN ENGLISH AS A SECOND LANGUAGE

How would you teach a Japanese student the diphthong [aɪ]? Does the German language have an [ɔɪ] phoneme? Can the [aʊ], so prevalent in American English, be taught to the French speaker without nasalization? These and other similar questions confront the instructor when attempting to handle the difficult problem of diphthongs in foreign accent.

Change is the characteristic feature of the diphthong. Change in pattern of sound as the speaker moves from one part of the speech signal to another has always been recognized in the dynamic approach to speech. Nowhere is this element of dynamic change in

> 51 Holbrook and Fairbanks (66:38-58) studied the five common diphthongs in terms of their formants and the dynamics of production. Bronstein (14:116-23, 186-204) discusses both diphthongs and triphthongs in American English.

speech better illustrated than in the diphthong or "vocalic cluster."

Vocalic cluster is used in the literature to describe a related group of two or more vowels used as a single distinctive sound unit or phoneme in a language. The first-person pronoun [aɪ] is an example of a diphthong, while Bronstein (*14*:116-23, 186-204) gives *mayor* [meɪɝ] as one sample of a triphthong in American English but adds, "These triphthongs are unstable in our language, however, often breaking into two syllables." Some authorities prefer to call this characteristic change within a vowel sound pattern a *glide*.

For students whose native language has only pure vowels, and glides from one sound to another are not permitted in the "standard" speech of the country, the diphthong presents an enigma. Their native tongues prevent their individual tongues from the necessary shifts in posture.

Portuguese, Spanish, Italian, German, and Norwegian have sounds similar to the diphthongs of English. However, not all of these languages use the diphthongs [ɑɪ], [eɪ], [ou], and [ɔɪ] as they are used in English. For example, the German language has additional variants of the diphthongs [ɑɪ], [ou], and [ɔɪ]; Italian uses such diphthongs as [ae], [ɛo], [ɛu], and [ɔa]; Norwegian has three diphthongs but only one, the [eɪ], is the same as the English diphthong. Such a condition compounds the difficulty of the second-language student whose native language is one which uses diphthongs. He hears a glide and attempts to reproduce it in terms of one of his native diphthongs; distortion frequently results.

Certain languages have no diphthongs. Although vowel sounds may appear together in a word or sound context, they are produced as individual sounds, sometimes as individual syllables as in the case of Japanese vowels. Every vowel in Japanese forms a separate syllable and the syllable may consist of a vowel by itself or a vowel preceded by a consonant in the CV pattern. When two vowels appear together in the same word as separate syllables, there is no change of position or glide in producing the sounds. When two similar vowels are together the sound of the first is merely lengthened without any glide characteristics being evident. Such a habit causes the student of American English to resist change of articulatory position when two vowels are produced together in a word such as *eat*. The tendency is to produce two individual sounds in substitution for [it] in attempts to speak English. In contrast, the words *boy, how,* and *line* are shortened from their native diphthong character to a single pure-vowel sound as in [bɔ], [hɑː], and [lɑn]. The same tendency is noted in [se] for [seɪ] and [no] for [nou] when the glide characteristic is omitted.

A similar characteristic is heard in the speech of the Hawaiian and Spanish speakers of English. When two vowels appear together in these languages, in such words as *baile* in Spanish and *lao* in Hawaiian, the speaker pauses briefly between the two sounds. Thus, the Spanish word meaning "to dance" becomes [bɑele] and the Hawaiian word for "iron" becomes [lɑ-o] in contrast to the diphthong in the English words *bile* and *now*. These students, as well as the French student who has no diphthongs in his native language, will have difficulty in learning to "slide" from one sound to another while maintaining a continuous flow of speech. These students will attempt to give each individual vowel its full value and a character-istic "syllabic" type of utterance becomes a factor in the foreign accent heard by the native speaker of English.

Thomas (138:258) says that the Chinese language has equivalents for all of the major English diphthongs except [ɔɪ], but the Chinese speaker regularly minimizes and often eliminates completely the second portion of the diphthong when speaking English as a second language. This situation is somewhat analogous to the diphthong problem encountered by the native speaker of Arabic when attempt-ing to speak English. Because Arabic "complex nuclei" are fewer in number than those in American English—in each case they are phonetically classified as *tense monophthongs*—they create a lan-guage problem. When the native speaker of Arabic attempts to learn American English speech, he substitutes these tense monophthongs for the diphthongs of English, thus giving a semblance of foreign accent to his English speech when evaluated by the native speaker in America.

Suggestions for Assisting the Foreign Student

Two of the vowel sounds of American English may be written as single sounds or as diphthongs when using phonetic symbols. Be-cause of the habit of students with various language backgrounds to use the tense monophthong as the Arabic student does or the pure vowel as the Hawaiian does, it is advisable when working with for-eign students to write the sounds [e] and [o] as the diphthongs [eɪ] and [oʊ]. Such a starting point for the discussion of vowel diphthong differences so prevalent in American English provides the student with a visual pattern of difference. Since there are two symbols, he associates the glide characteristic of diphthong production with the visual symbols and the concept is usually more readily accepted. Arrows indicating different directions of pitch change used with the diphthongs are useful in assisting the student to understand move-ment characteristics of diphthongs. For example, *I* may be [ɑɪ] ↗ or [ɑɪ] ↘, *oh* may be presented as [oʊ] ↗, [oʊ] ↘, [oʊ] ⌒ , or [oʊ] ⌄ . Van Riper* gives a glimpse of the experience a French student had with the English diphthongs.

> Gaston had studied English in Paris and managed to be barely intelli-gible in ordinary communication. One day he came to us, his face alight

* Personal communication from Charles Van Riper, September 1963.

with excitement, his gestures flaying about in all directions, and at first we could not understand what he was trying to tell us. Finally, we gathered that he had discovered the diphthongs we use instead of the pure vowels [e] and [o]. [ɑɪ hɑv fɑʊ zis sikrɛt zi əmerɪkɑ pɛrso ze ɑr zi wʊlf læk zis ouuuu ze se souuu æn nouuu æn ouuu]. Gaston howled like a wolf each time he spoke these vowels.

Although it is understood that there are no minimal pairs which contrast these sounds, the clinician may find it advantageous in contrasting the production of the foreign-language student and the native American speaker.

> 52 The status of [e], [eɪ], [o], and [oʊ] in phonetics and linguistics has been the subject of varying opinions delivered orally or in writing. Wise (153:17-18, 95-100, 107-8, 115) presents the treatment of all four sounds as single vowels and diphthongs. Heffner (62:110-12, 146-50) calls [ei] and [oʊ] *diphthongal vowels* and describes their relationship to [e] and [o].

Methods suggested in the vowel study section of this chapter, using nonsense syllables, word symbols, and sentences, may be used as effectively with diphthongs in English. Paired words such as *bet/bait, mit/mate, putt/pate,* contrasting the closely associated vowel sounds [ɛ], [ɪ], and [ʌ] with [eɪ] may assist the student in appreciating the length and glide characteristics of the diphthongs of American English. Contrast words in lists are available for clinicians and teachers in the books of the bibliography.

> 53 Contrast words and exercises for improving skill in use of diphthongs in American English are available in Fairbanks (36:87-96), Carrell and Tiffany (21:234-37), and Leutenegger (94:54-57).

Once the student has acquired the ability to make a discrimination necessary to hear the difference between pure vowel and a diphthong or glide when isolated sounds or sounds in contrast words are used, he is ready for practice in distinguishing between two diphthongs in closely related words. This accomplishment should not require extensive practice, but students differ in their ability to accomplish such discrimination.

Having established the ability to discriminate between these sound elements, the pure vowel and the diphthong and two diphthongs of different characteristics, the student is prepared for production practice. Some clinicians and teachers prefer to distribute production practice with varying degrees of ear training, but the time used in developing adequate auditory discrimination will frequently be well repaid in rapid production practice.

The Paratore (114) dialogues will provide conversational drill in a structured form. Directions for use of the dialogues and the marking system used are presented in the preface to the text.

Vowels and diphthongs of American English prove difficult for the second-language learner, because they are difficult to "see" and almost impossible to "feel" when they are being produced. The same may be said of the time and duration factors of American English. Since sound patterns, the number of these sounds produced within a given time, and the duration of the sounds and pauses are individual characteristics of any language, they prove to be hurdles for the second-language learner. The fine differences in resonant quality between native vowels of some languages and those of English make the discrimination of differences difficult for the student in *listening* or in *feedback* when produced in the stream of speech. An instructor or clinician becomes the critical ear in evaluating the successful production of new vowels and diphthongs until such time as electronic and mechanical equipment is available for providing better discrimination and visual reproduction.

Consonant Problems in Learning American English

The sounds of speech commonly called *consonants* are the result of audible friction or stopping of the breath in some part of the mouth or throat. The simplest division of consonant sounds is into obstruents and sonorants, as indicated by Hockett (63:93-101). A more complicated system will divide the sounds of consonants into eight or more classifications on the basis of physiological production and at least an equal number of divisions on the basis of acoustic characteristics.

Kaiser (76:317-29) presents the European method of classification. Wise (153:17-18, 95-100, 107-8, 115) uses the most recent conventional pairing of voiced and voiceless consonants in his acoustic classification of consonants.

It would be helpful to the clinician and teacher to be able to say that there are some consonant sounds in American English which do not create trouble for the foreign speaker or polyglot. As the clinician acquires more experience with various language backgrounds, he soon discovers that all sounds of English are problem sounds for some speakers. The *b* in *boy* appears to be so simple and easily produced that the native assumes that no one else produces it in any other way. When he begins to learn Spanish or works in the clinic where the bilabial fricative is used for the [b], the clinician comes to realize that there are many ways to produce the sound of *b*. German has sounds represented by the letters *b, d, g, b,* and *z;* yet they are used in different distribution or positions than those in which they appear in English, and sound changes accompany these changed positions. Arabic has letters and sounds for *t, d, s, z, n, l,* and *r,* but in every case they are produced as dental sounds, while American English produces them as alveolar sounds. In Russian the sounds [ʃ], [ʒ], and [dʒ] appear as a part of native speech, but the [ʃ] and [ʒ] are produced much farther back than in English, thus creating a distortion of sound when produced. As a language sound the [dʒ] appears infrequently in Russian, but the occurrence of the sound in English in the medial and final position of many words causes the nonnative speaker to substitute other more familiar sounds or to distort the [dʒ]. Our catalogue of variations in the consonant sounds of English and foreign languages, represented by the same letter but containing innumerable fine sound differences which create confusion, could be extended throughout the entire list of American English phonemes. Each sound presents a problem to some second-language learner. The proper analysis of each problem begins with an evaluation of the American English of each student, followed by a comparison with the sound patterns of the native language. Such a contrastive analysis of each of the elements of the two languages should indicate the areas of need in therapy or in classwork.

> 56   The contrastive analyses of English and several other languages have
>   recently been made available for the second-language teacher. Moulton
>   (108) provides the systematic analysis of the contrasts between the German
>   and English sound systems.

Since space does not allow for the discussion of all problems to be encountered by the student in learning American English consonants, three sound groups have been selected. The voiced and voiceless *th* sounds [ð] and [θ] represent the interdental consonant difficulties which appear in the clinic or classroom. From the nasal consonants the [ŋ] was selected, since it offers the most severe challenge to the nonnative speaker. Finally, the [r] in all its various shadings represents the semivowel or glide which, at times, takes on full vowel form in [ɝ] and [ɚ] as used in General American English. Each foreign speaker has difficulty in coping with these unruly *r* sounds.

The *th* Sounds [ð] *and* [θ]

The dental fricative in both voiced and voiceless form is prominent in American English. It is missing from the Slavonic languages, Italian, and the Scandinavian languages, as well as Gaelic, but still occurs in the speech of Iceland, Norway, Denmark, Spain, and Greece. Whatever may be the basic cause of the absence of this sound from these certain middle and southern language groups, the students from these countries do not use the [ð] and [θ] and have difficulty acquiring the sound in American English speech.

Both sounds appear in the initial, medial, and final positions in words of English. Substitution of a native sound is the most common method of handling the problem, and the substitution of [d] for the voiced form in such words as *there, although,* and *breathe* usually occurs. In the final position the sound is unvoiced by some native speakers and polyglots, making *breathe, teethe,* and *lathe* end with the [θ] and, thus, changing the word in meaning as well as in form.

German speakers substitute the [z] for the voiced sound [ð] and the [s] for [θ], the unvoiced form of *th*. Some authorities indicate that these substitutions are more prevalent among the educated Germans who will say [zɪs iz oke wɪs mi]. Less well educated Germans will say [dɪs iz oke wɪt mi]. Among the less well educated Germans the [d] and [t] are substituted for the [ð] and [θ] of American English words. The Arabic student substitutes the [s] and the [z] in the same manner as the educated German speaker, but the habit appears to be consistent among all speakers of the language. Chinese natives use the [s] as a substitute for the voiceless *th* sound; so they say [sɪn] for *thin* or [wɪs] for *with,* but the sound is frequently distorted in the direction of [ʃ] and you may hear [gɪv mi e ʃɪn slaɪʃ ʌv mit].

Among the polyglot speakers of Polish, Hungarian, Spanish, and Indian languages, the [d] and [t] are the most consistent substitutions for [ð] and [θ]. "Dis is my mudder" has been frequently heard by clinicians and teachers in the schools and clinics of American urban centers, in the backwoods areas of the mountains and about the pueblos of the Western Plains. It frequently becomes the sound key to the label "substandard speech," as well as serving as a symptom of foreign accent.

Exercises concentrating on the establishment of the interdental fricative sounds in both voiced and unvoiced forms will be simplified by the visual and tactical cues which may be used to establish the sound. Clinicians and teachers accustomed to using the mirror for speech therapy will find this sound rather easy to establish in isolation.

Contrast drills using [t], [d], [s], [z], and [f] and [v] will assist the student to discriminate the difference in frictional sound produced when the [θ] and [ð] are produced. The drills provided by clinicians for the interdental lisp will be useful for teaching foreign students the auditory discrimination and sound production contrasts necessary for establishing the [θ] and [ð].

57   Van Riper and Irwin (145:77-83, 105-163) illustrate the common errors
      of the [s] phoneme and give a thorough treatment of handling articu-
      lation problems. Fairbanks (36:87-96) provides contrast drills.

The Nasal Sound [ŋ]

When the native American English speaker produces the final sound in *sing* or the medial [ŋ] in *bringing,* he produces a sound which, to the ear of the uninitiated, sounds strangely like "two different sounds." Several problems appear in the clinic when attempting to teach this new sound. *First,* the development of an intrusive [g] creates an *additional* problem for the foreign speaker. He says, "I am sing-ging" [aɪ æm sɪŋ gɪŋ]. *Second,* the omission of the back tongue "klang" in the sound causes the substitution of an [n] as a competitive nasal for the [ŋ]. *Finally,* an attempt to produce the nasalization among certain students creates a distorted sound which resembles the [m]. American Indian students frequently produce this sound when attempting to use the final [ŋ] as well as the final [n]. They may use the expression [ðə wɪməm wɝ sɪŋʔəm] when they mean that *the women were singing.* It may be from such substitutions that writers of paperback novels adopted the excessive use of [əm] in the speech of Indian characters.

Presence of the sound in the medial and final position in American English, except in modern loan words such as Ngana and Ngbaka, makes it a two-position problem. The absence of the sound [ŋ] in French, Russian, Navajo, Italian, and Polish often creates real difficulty in its production by such speakers. The fact that several of these languages have a [ɲ] sound of phonemic value in their speech leads to additional confusion in production when attempts to produce the [ŋ] in *sing, bring,* or *sprinkle* are made. They say these facts point up the importance of a contrastive evaluation of

the native language with the sounds of American language in the
area óf nasal consonants when specific study of the [ŋ] is in progress.

Difficulties with the American English

The variety of *r* sounds of our language produces problems not
only for native American children and adults, but also for students
of English as a second language. Difficulties of foreign students

58 Heffner (62) reviews the *r*-sounds in foreign languages and in American
English.

result from distribution of the *r* in the various languages of the
world, the form of sound production employed in producing the *r*,
and the semivowel character of the sound in certain languages.

You may have attempted to learn the German uvular *r* [ʀ], the
trilled *r* [r̃] of Scottish, or the tap trill of Spanish [ɾ]. As you struggle
to make your uvula operate as a vibrator or force your tongue to
"flap," you can appreciate the problems of the speaker who has acquired such skill over a period of years, attempting to retract the
tongue for the production of an *r* sound. Perhaps the most difficult
task of the clinician or teacher is teaching the new sound in isolation. Grasping this concept of an *r* sound produced without vibra-
tory activity of some part of the articulatory mechanism baffles some
students of the second language. Words such as *red,* since the initial
[r] * is rolled in many languages, *fairer,* because the combination of
a medial [r] and a final [r] are produced with different types of
vibration in some languages, and *her,* because a post-vocalic [r] is
sometimes omitted in certain languages all create problems for the
new American English speaker.

When Heinrich Martin came to the laboratory he was struggling with
the General American [r]. He was a conscientious worker and had a
good ear for sound variations, but the battle of the *r* proved too much
for him. One day he appeared in the office of the director, his face
flushed and clothes disheveled. Struggling with the principles taught, he
sputtered, [dɪz əmɛrɪkæn R-R-R-R]. He spit out the uvular *r* of his
native German, [mɪz hɪtomɪ ʃi ze lɛd, lɛd loz ‖ mɪstə vənɛlɪ ze wɛd,

* The International Phonetic alphabet uses the [ɹ] for the "fric-
tionless continuant and semivowel" *r,* but for purposes of sim-
plicity and in accordance with the practice of other writers in the
field, the [r] symbol will be used throughout this text to represent
the General American continuant semivowel *r.* For the retroflex
central vowel, the [ɝ] and [ɚ] will be used.

wɛd, woz ‖ ɑɪ ze Rɛd Rɛd Roz ‖ vɑɪ don zi əmɛrɪkæn lɑɪk zɪvɪlɑɪzd pœpl]. He expressed the feelings of many second-language learners regarding the General American r.

Difficulties also appear in the initial, medial, and final positions in the stream of speech. The types of changes which appear are sound omissions, sound additions, sound substitutions, and sound distortions. Sound substitutions, primarily the substitution of the native [r], will be the most prevalently heard in the clinic or classroom. Among the Orientals the [l] substitution for the [r] has become such a problem in the clinic and classroom that some clinicians suspect that there is an anatomical or physiological reason for the inability to produce the sound. In this they agree with Brosnahan's hypothesis yet to be established.

Because [r] is probably the most variable of all the consonants in American English, it will present problems for the second-language learner in all positions and in all types of connected discourse.

> 59   Bronstein (14:116-23, 186-204) presents [r] as one of the frictionless
>   consonants and reviews the use of the sound in parts of the United
>   States and Canada.

How the sound is taught will depend upon what dialect area of the United States the student chooses for his instruction. The form and distribution of the sound will be different in the Eastern, Southern, and General American dialect areas, but these variations will be minor compared to the needs of the student in relearning the [r] for American English. The reader is asked to consult general phonetic texts listed in the bibliography for differences in the [r] in American English.

Establishing the American English [r] in the speech of the second-language learner involves learning a consonant form and a vowel form. The difficulty encountered by the Chinese in handling the [r] and [l] sounds of English by substitution of [l] for [r] is well known in the clinics where Chinese students learn English. Sam Yee says, [fɔl sɔl ænd sɛvən jiəz əgo ɑl foləfɑðəz....] as he reproduces the opening lines of the Gettysburg Address. Here, one semivowel is substituted for another and the "wavering of the tongue position" is attributed as the cause of the difference in some instances. Shen (127:47-55) offers a method of teaching the initial r to Chinese students which should prove useful to the clinician and the teacher. It has been used in teaching the r to other Oriental and non-Oriental students.

In teaching the vowel *r* the student must be made cognizant of the glide form of the sound in such words as *fear, car,* and *dart.* The vowelized *r* used most consistently in General American speech is represented by the symbol [ɝ] in the stressed position in words such as *bird, heard,* and *turn.* For the foreign student accustomed to pure vowels, the glide *r* offers double difficulty. He must first produce a new sound and then he must learn to glide into another position in order to use the sound syllabically. The vowelized *r* creates somewhat less trouble as the students learning American English have frequently been exposed to British English and have established a semblance of *r*-colored vowels. For the beginner the vowel form of [r] symbolized by [ɝ] and [ɚ] offers one appropriate place to begin the attack on the *r.*

Speech is composed of sounds that have distinctive characteristics which distinguish one group of noises from another. When these distinctive sounds are associated in certain patterns, they become units capable of taking on meaning. As we learn a language our ear becomes accustomed to discriminating these distinctive characteristics, one from another. In our discussion of American English speech we have named three classes or types of sounds present in various languages: vowels, diphthongs, and consonants, using the names most consistently given these classes in the field of speech.

COMMUNICATIVE SPEECH IS MORE THAN SOUND, SILENCE, AND PATTERNS of arrangement. Speech is idea and meaning; oral communication has purpose. Man retains the image of experience and in his practice of probing the attic of memory, he has the word symbol to assist him. When the elder transfers the results of his experience to his sons and daughters, word symbols form the coinage of the time-binding process. The idea communicated by these words often has more significance than is inherent in the literal translation of the words used. Because of this, the same language tool that facilitates retention of native experiences becomes a barrier to the second-language learner. Concepts and images called up by the sounds of

speech and the idiom
in foreign accent

a native language are distorted when the word symbols in a new tongue are translated literally. The idiom of American English speech is part of the required learning program if the nonnative speaker is to speak without a foreign accent.

The first-, as well as the second-, language learner begins his speech development by experimenting with the sounds and patterns of tone. Listening, producing, and associating are stages of speech development dependent upon an adequate ability to hear, to discriminate, and to learn patterns in association and arrangement of symbols for communication. Learning to recognize and use these distinctive differences is not enough. Native speech includes *understanding* what is said.

LANGUAGE AND UNDERSTANDING

Understanding the speaker of American English and producing American speech requires more than the use of mechanical skills acquired by generalization and discrimination. Meaningful speech includes the recognition and use of three features having semantic

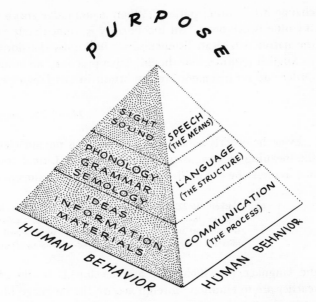

Figure 10. The Speech Pattern—Monolingual, Bilingual, Polyglot.

value: individual word meanings, ideas contained in word arrangements, and idiomatic expressions.

First, Vocabulary Is Essential

Our student speaker of American English should have a listening-speaking vocabulary to support the reading-writing vocabulary with which he usually appears in the clinic. Since reading and writing develop most naturally out of speech, the oral use of language should be taught first, according to modern language theory. Meaning

60 Hattori (57:207-12) points out that the meaning of a sentence is not the sum of the meaning of words in a phrase, clause, or sentence, but something greater than any of these.

is inherent in an efficient human-communication system, whether the symbolic form is oral or written.

Second, Words Appear in Patterns

Because each language has an arrangement of word symbols peculiar to its speech, the second-language learner may be required to change his habitual pattern. When a nonnative speaker says, "The sky blue is overhead," an incongruity is immediately recognized by the native American listener, since he knows the normal sequence in English requires that the adjective precedes the noun it modifies. Order and arrangement are important in any language.

Third, Language Has Idiom

Even the orderly arrangement of words is not sufficient to express the meaning of some expressions in speech. Literal translations do not express the idea. Idiomatic forms are private and peculiar to

61   Hockett (65:222-29) describes the formation of idioms in language and explains their characteristics. Yandell (154) has studied the difficulties encountered by students learning English as a second language when idiomatic expressions are encountered in reading elementary materials.

the language in which they are developed. If the therapist and teacher are to eliminate foreign accent, the language idiom must be understood and taught as a part of recognizing distinctive differences in meaning.

Idiomatic expressions, whether they are such simple American English parts of words as *plane* for *airplane, cello* for *violoncello,* or *phone* for *telephone* or whether they are multiple word patterns, are constantly being created in any language. The student who learns to "speak like a native" should learn to identify such idioms as, "I escaped by *the skin of my teeth,"* and "There is more than one way *to skin a cat."* Their mechanical acquisition is not the important item, but the understanding of their intrinsic value for interpreting the language background of the speaker is essential. The richness of any language is contained in the meanings that lie below the surface. Idioms reveal the subtlety of meaning contained in the words, phrases, and sentences of a language. When the student can recognize idioms, interpret their meanings, and produce them in the proper setting, he will be acquiring native control of the idiom in speech.

Besides the usual recognition and practice drills, the use of conversational reading passages, or the playing of colloquial roles, there are three other major methods for helping our foreign students to acquire the sense of structure and idiom. These are: (*a*) parallel talking in which the clinician verbalizes for the student the thoughts and perceptions he is having at the very instant, (*b*) shadowing or echo speech, in which the student echoes almost simultaneously what his clinician is saying, and (c) the delayed pantomimic or subvocal rehearsal of what the teacher has just said.

> 62 These techniques are described in some detail in Van Riper (144:146-48, 242-305). Shadowing is described by Marland (98:242-45).

Fourth, Culture Influences Speech

Speech is a social form of communication and, therefore, the highest level of meaning will come from the interpretation of meaningful units in terms of the society that speaks the language. Every society values *speech* and *silence* in different proportions. There are the gregarious talkative societies. Americans are frequently classed in this group. There are also the silent listeners, and the American Indian is usually typified as belonging to the silent group. Between these extremes are all shades of *quantity* of sound or silence in speech.

There is a qualitative difference in speech which is determined by the culture that produces the language.

> 63 Brooks (15:81-93) defines culture and suggests ways of orienting the student to language patterns of any culture.

Let us summarize the steps in listening to, and understanding, American English speech.

1. The status of the student's hearing has been investigated and proper adjustment has been made for any hearing deficiency.
2. An evaluation of the individual's listening vocabulary has established the level at which work should begin.
3. The student's understanding of the patterns and structures in which words appear in American English has been ascertained, and his ability to interpret the meaning of such structural forms is adequate for the program.
4. The idiomatic speech and special reference words in American English have been practiced in listening and producing exercises. Discussion of meaning has been associated consistently with the idiomatic expressions and vocabulary items.

PRODUCING CULTURAL EXPERIENCES

There is no way to obtain cultural experiences by reading about them in a test. Although the information obtained in this manner is valuable for any student, it will never substitute for speaking and listening in the conversational, business, or formal public-address situation. For this reason the program of therapy for foreign students at this level involves practical experiences in social situations utilizing the principles learned.

1. Greetings and items of social exchange are among the first automatic responses which could be taught. From the patterned drills which the students have already perfected, it should be possible to move to discussion of special contrasts in modes of greeting. Questions and statements used when making purchases, obtaining food in the cafeteria, books in the bookstore, periodicals at the library, and similar exchanges commonly used in American English should be a part of the therapy program.

2. Oral skills for immediate use in the classroom, the home, and on the job should be introduced into the classroom or the clinic. If the student is in a school program at elementary school, junior or senior high school, college, or graduate school, the needs of his speech will be those which will serve him at the level in which he will be functioning. The questions may be asked: How do I respond to roll call? How should I address the instructor? Even, what should I wear to class? A part of the foreign accent problem is contained in the inability of the student to phrase such questions and statements in the second-language form. Relying on translation from the native language, our student asks questions or responds in terms of native speech structure and the listener realizes this is nonnative speech.

3. How do I buy groceries at the supermarket? What do I say when I wish to open a charge account in the department store on the corner? How do banks function in America? These and similar questions are constantly being asked by adult students in the United States. They are practical questions for the second-language student who is anxious to adjust as rapidly as possible.

4. In addition to the demands of practical life, existing in a culture are those contacts provided by leisure activities, aesthetic pleasures, religious obligations, and political institutions. The process of voting at an election has always been an interesting facet of American life for the students of voting age. Discussion of the American system, demonstration of the voting machine, and a trip to a polling place during one of the regular elections has proved fruitful. Similarly, visits to the art gallery, anthropology museum, geology museum, and the rare-book room of the library have provided the impetus for stimulating conversation from some of the most silent members of the class during structured drill. When the subject of

the experience touches their talent area or their professional interest, the student will often struggle to express himself in his new language.

5. Oral production of drama, literature, and debate will stimulate reactions from the students, as well as introduce them to the products of the American English culture. Often the nonnative student receives the impression that Americans are shallow, uninterested in "higher-level" discussions of philosophy, literature of the day, music, and poetry. Our busy daily lives appear to de-emphasize this part of American English conversation. Since it does exist and is enjoyed by large numbers of English-speaking people, it should be revealed as a part of life outside the classroom. Visits to the little theater or commercial theater in the area, attendance at the lecture series provided by the University or the local chamber of commerce will provide a starting point for discussion. The educational television station in any area provides usable programs of this type, as well as instructional offerings. Each presentation will form the nucleus for discussion of some aspect of American English culture and the use of oral language in a different setting.

6. Finally, every culture has certain taboos, cultural practices, contrasting ways of behaving that puzzle strangers. Once the student has been oriented to the positive cultural activities and their impact on oral communication, these negative aspects might be demonstrated and discussed.

> 64 Hall (50) introduces the importance of cultural features in learning the "total" language.

The student with a foreign accent needs this exposure to the cultural backgrounds of American English. Clinicians and teachers have found that the polyglot student, born and educated in the United States, is culturally impoverished. This cultural poverty is more damaging in his speech development than to the speech development of the student who comes from another country. For those readers who enjoy skin diving, the needs of the student with a foreign accent might be compared to your experiences in learning the art of underwater investigation.

Remember that when you had just learned to paddle in your favorite pool, lake, or ocean, it was a struggle merely to remain on the surface. Frequently, in your efforts to remember the fundamentals, you lost your equilibrium and swallowed a mouthful of water. With constant practice and what seemed an unnecessary number of immersions you learned to do the crawl, the backstroke, the side-stroke, and the float. Somehow you had put together the units learned into something resembling a synergy. These structural patterns of movement enabled you to pull yourself through the water to "go places" or you could float leisurely on the surface watching the sky and the clouds.

As confidence developed you soon began to swim out beyond the sight of land or dive below the surface, leaving the security of your native air-land existence behind. At first you returned rapidly to the surface and to the familiar landmarks of sky and air. But as experience increased, the spirit of daring came with it and you were soon discovering the beauties of the depths. Weeds, coral, fish, and sea urchins, suspended or scattered throughout that luminous liquid through which you could drift at your leisure, tell you of the strange life below the surface and invite you to come back.

Having sampled the thrills of skin diving, you soon became enamored of the depths. Completely at home in this new environment, you now can enjoy the pleasures of investigation hidden from the beginner. With skill comes an appreciation of these hidden values. You have become "infected" with the sport of skin diving.

Our second-language students will have a similar experience if our work in the clinic or classroom is effective and stimulating. The need to learn the fundamentals of sound production, intonational variation, and effective use of stress and rhythm as automatic reactions to be used in listening and producing American English is of prime importance. In addition, the student who would enjoy the language and make it a part of his everyday life must acquire the idiom and become immersed in the culture of his second-language environment.

If the clinician or teacher is able to give his students a glimpse of this ultimate goal, he provides motivation. As he drills and analyzes, compares and contrasts the native language and the second language, the student frequently becomes discouraged by the feeling of hopelessness imposed by speech and language *interference*. He misses the magic of "second-language learning" and realizes that it is often dull and routine unless it can be sparked from within. The life and literature of any language is filled with material to peak the imagination of the learner. If we are to go beneath the surface of the foreign accent which we hear to help the student, this type of motivation will be needed.

bibliography

1. Albright, Joy S., and Robert W. Albright, "The Role of Linguistics in Speech and Hearing Therapy," *Language Learning*, IX (1959), 51-55.

2. Alger, Doris, Materials duplicated for use in the Workshop on Second-Language Teaching (June 11-22, 1962), Division of Indian Education, New Mexico State Department of Education.

3. Anderson, Virgil A., *Training of the Speaking Voice* (New York: Oxford University Press, 1961).

4. Anshen, Ruth N., "Language an Idea," *Language: An Enquiry Into Its Meaning and Function* (New York: Harper & Row, Publishers, Inc., 1957).

5. Berko, Jean, "The Child's Learning of English Morphology," *Word*, XIV (1958).

6. Berlo, David K., *The Process of Communication* (New York: Holt, Rinehart & Winston, Inc., 1960), pp. 23-28.

7. Berry, Mildred, and Jon Eisenson, *Speech Disorders* (New York: Appleton-Century-Crofts, Inc., 1956).

8. Black, John W., and Wilbur E. Moore, *Speech, Code, Meaning and Communication* (New York: McGraw-Hill Book Company, 1955).

9. Bolinger, Dwight, "Intonation: Levels Versus Configuration," *Word*, VII (December 1951).

10. ———, "Stress and Information," *American Speech*, XXXIII (February 1958).

11. Bower, William A., *International Manual of Linguists and Translators*, First Supplement (New York: The Scarecrow Press, Inc., 1961).

12. Brain, Lord D. M., F.R.C.P., *Speech Disorders: Aphasia, Apraxia and Agnosia* (Washington, D.C.: Butterworth & Co., 1961).

13. Brong, C. Cordelia, "An Evaluation of Ear Training as a Pedagogical Technique in Improving Sound Discrimination" (unpublished doctoral dissertation), Northwestern University, 1948.
14. Bronstein, Arthur J., *The Pronunciation of American English* (New York: Appleton-Century-Crofts, 1960).
15. Brooks, Nelson, *Language and Language Learning* (New York: Harcourt, Brace & World, Inc., 1960).
16. Brown, Roger, *Words and Things* (Glencoe, Ill.: The Free Press, 1958).
17. Bunch, C. C., *Clinical Audiometry* (St. Louis: The C. V. Mosby Company, 1943).
18. Burssens, A., "Notes on African Tone Languages," *Manual of Phonetics,* L. Kaiser, ed. (Amsterdam: North-Holland Publishing Company, 1947).
19. Campbell, G. A., "Telephonic Intelligibility," *London, Edinburgh, Dublin, Philosophical Magazine and Journal of Science,* XIX (January 1910).
20. Carrell, James A., "A Comparative Study of Speech Defective Children" (unpublished doctoral dissertation), Northwestern University, 1946.
21. Carrell, James, and William Tiffany, *Phonetics: Theory and Application to Speech Improvement* (New York: McGraw-Hill Book Company, 1960).
22. Carroll, John B., *The Study of Languages: A Survey of Linguistics and Related Disciplines in America* (Cambridge, Mass.: Harvard University Press, 1953).
23. Carrow, Sister Mary, "Linguistic Functioning of Bilingual and Monolingual Children," *Journal of Speech and Hearing Disorders,* XXII (1957).
24. Cartright, Richard W., "On Machines and Men," *The Southern Speech Journal,* XXVIII (Summer 1963).
25. Chaiklin, Joseph B., "Native American Listeners' Adaptation in Understanding Speakers with Foreign Dialect," *Journal of Speech and Hearing Disorders,* XX (June 1955).
26. Chomsky, Noam, *Syntactic Structures* (The Hague: Mouton and Company, 1957).
27. Coffee, Nathaniel M., "The Phonemic Structure of Unstressed Vowels in English," *American Speech,* XXVI (February 1951), No. 1.
28. Curtis, James F., and James C. Hardy, "Cite Importance to Therapy of Regarding Phoneme as Articulatory Event," from Letters to the Editor, *Journal of Speech and Hearing Research,* IV (June 1961).
29. Darley, Frederic L., and Harris Winitz, "Age of First Word-Review of Research," *Journal of Speech and Hearing Disorders,* XXVI (August 1961).
30. Davis, Hallowell, *Hearing and Deafness,* Revised Ed. (New York: Holt, Rinehart & Winston, Inc., 1960).
31. De Grott, A. W., "Phonetics and Its Relation to Aesthetics," *Manual of Phonetics,* L. Kaiser, ed. (Amsterdam: North-Holland Publishing Company, 1957).

32. De Saussure, Ferdinand, *Course in General Linguistics* (New York: Philosophical Library, Inc., 1959).

33. Eisenson, Jon, *Stuttering: A Symposium* (New York: Harper & Row, Publishers, Inc., 1958).

34. *English Sentence Pattern Drills for Beginning Indian Children,* Division of Indian Education, New Mexico State Department of Education, Santa Fe, New Mexico, 1962.

35. Evans, Bergen, "Grammar for Today," *Introductory Readings on the English Language,* Richard Braddock, ed. (Englewood Cliffs, N.J.: Prentice-Hall, Inc., 1962).

36. Fairbanks, Grant, *Voice and Articulation Drill Book,* 2nd Ed. (New York: Harper & Row, Publishers, Inc., 1960).

37. Finocchiaro, Mary, *Teaching English as a Second Language: In Elementary and Secondary Schools* (New York: Harper & Row, Publishers, Inc., 1958).

38. Fischer-Jorgensen, Eli, "What Can the New Techniques of Acoustic Phonetics Contribute to Linguistics," *Psycholinguistics,* Sol Saporta, ed. (New York: Holt, Rinehart & Winston, Inc., 1961).

39. Fletcher, H., and J. C. Steinberg, "Articulation Testing Methods," *Bell System Technical Journal,* VIII (1929).

40. Flint, Kathleen Dush, *English for New Americans* (Philadelphia: Chilton Company Book Division, 1960).

41. Fogelquist, Donald F., "The Bilingualism of Paraguay," *Hispania,* XXXIII (1950).

42. Follet, Wilson, "Bargain Basement English," *Introductory Readings on the English Language,* Richard Braddock, ed. (Englewood Cliffs, N.J.: Prentice-Hall, Inc., 1962).

43. Francis, W. Nelson, *The Structure of American English* (New York: The Ronald Press Company, 1958).

44. Fries, Charles, *An Intensive Course in English for Latin-American Students* (Ann Arbor, Mich.: English Language Institute, University of Michigan Press, 1947).

45. ———, "Meaning and Linguistic Analysis," *Readings in Applied Linguistics,* Harold B. Allen, ed. (New York: Appleton-Century-Crofts, 1958).

46. Fry, D. B., "Perception and Recognition in Speech," *For Roman Jakobson,* Morris Halle, *et al.,* eds. (The Hague: Mouton and Company, 1596).

47. Glanzer, Murray, "Toward a Psychology of Language Structure," *Journal of Speech and Hearing Research,* V (December 1962).

48. Gordon, Morton J., and Helene H. Wong, *A Manual for Speech Improvement* (Englewood Cliffs, N.J.: Prentice-Hall, Inc., 1961).

49. Gray, Giles W., and Claude M. Wise, *The Bases of Speech,* 3rd Ed. (New York: Harper & Row, Publishers, Inc., 1959).

50. Hall, Edward, *The Silent Language* (Garden City, N.Y.: Doubleday & Company, Inc., 1959).

51. Hall, Margaret E., "Auditory Factors in Functional Articulatory Speech Defects," (doctoral dissertation), State University of Iowa, 1936, *Journal of Experimental Education,* VII (1938-1939).

52. Hall, Robert A., Jr., *Linguistics and Your Language*, 2nd Revised Ed. (Garden City, N.Y.: Doubleday & Company, Inc., 1950).

53. Hanley, Theodore D., and Wayne L. Thurman, *Developing Vocal Skills* (New York: Holt, Rinehart & Winston, Inc., 1962).

54. ——, *Student Projects for Developing Vocal Skills* (New York: Holt, Rinehart & Winston, Inc., 1962).

55. Hansen, Burrell F., "The Application of Sound Discrimination Tests to Functional Articulatory Defects" (unpublished master's thesis), Purdue University, 1942.

56. Harms, L. S., "Programmed Learning for the Field of Speech," *The Speech Teacher*, X (September 1961).

57. Hattori, Shiro, "The Analysis of Meaning," *For Roman Jakobson* (The Hague: Mouton and Company, 1956).

58. Haugen, Einar, *Bilingualism in the Americas: A Bibliography and Research Guide*, Publication of the American Dialect Society, No. 26 (University, Alabama: University of Alabama Press, 1956).

59. ——, "The Bilingual Community," *Bilingualism in the Americas: A Bibliography and Research Guide*, Publication of the American Dialect Society No. 26 (University, Alabama: University of Alabama Press, 1956).

60. ——, "The Bilingual Individual," *Psycholinguists*, Sol Saporta, ed. (New York: Holt, Rinehart & Winston, Inc., 1961).

61. ——, "Language in Contact," *Proceedings of the VIII International Congress of Linguists* (Oslo: Oslo University Press, 1958).

62. Heffner, R-M. S., *General Phonetics* (Madison, Wis.: The University of Wisconsin Press, 1952).

63. Hockett, Charles, *A Course in Modern Linguistics* (New York: The Macmillan Company, 1958).

64. ——, "Logical Considerations in the Study of Animal Communication," *Animal Sounds and Communication*, W. E. Lanyon and W. N. Tavolga, eds. (American Institute of Biological Sciences, Washington, D.C., 1960).

65. ——, "Idiom Formation," *For Roman Jakobson* (The Hague: Mouton and Company, 1956).

66. Holbrook, Anthony, and Grant Fairbanks, "Diphthong Formants and Their Movements," *Journal of Speech and Hearing Research*, V (March 1962).

67. Hornsby, A. S., E. V. Gatenby, and H. Wakefield, *Advanced Learner's Dictionary of Current English* (New York: Oxford University Press, 1960).

68. Hubbell, Allan F., "The Phonemic Analysis of Unstressed Vowels," *American Speech*, XXV (1950).

69. Hughes, John P., *The Science of Language* (New York: Random House, Inc., 1962).

69a. Humphrey, William R., and Robert Milisen, "A Study of the Ability to Reproduce Unfamiliar Sounds Which Have Been Presented Orally," *Journal of Speech and Hearing Disorders*, Monograph Supplement, No. 4 (December 1954).

70. Johnson, F. Craig, and Kenneth Frandsen, "Administering the

Brown-Carlsen Listening Comprehension Test," *The Journal of Communication,* XIII (March 1963).

71. Johnson, Wendell, *The Onset of Stuttering* (Minneapolis: University of Minnesota Press, 1959).

72. Jones, Daniel, *The Pronunciation of English,* 3rd Ed. (Cambridge, England: The University Press, 1950).

73. Joos, Martin, *Acoustic Phonetics,* Language Monograph 23 (Baltimore: Waverly Press, 1948).

74. ———, "Description of Language Design," *Journal of the Acoustical Society of America,* XXII (1950).

75. ———, "Semology: A Linguistic Theory of Meaning," *Studies in Linguistics,* XIII (Winter 1958).

76. Kaiser, L., ed., *Manual of Phonetics* (Amsterdam: North-Holland Publishing Company, 1957).

77. Kantner, Claude E., and Robert West, *Phonetics,* Rev. Ed. (New York: Harper & Row, Publishers, Inc., 1960).

78. Kaplan, Harold M., *Anatomy and Physiology of Speech* (New York: McGraw-Hill Book Company, 1960).

79. Keenan, Joseph S., "What is Medial Position?" *Journal of Speech and Hearing Disorders,* XXVI (May 1961).

80. Kenyon, John S., *American Pronunciation* (Ann Arbor, Mich.: George Wahr, Publisher, 1946).

81. ———, and Thomas A. Knott, *A Pronouncing Dictionary of American English* (Springfield, Mass.: G. & C. Merriam Company, 1944).

82. Krasner, Leonard, "Studies of the Conditioning of Verbal Behavior," *Psycholinguistics,* Sol Saporta, ed. (New York: Holt, Rinehart & Winston, Inc., 1961).

83. Kurath, Hans, *A Word Geography of the Eastern United States* (Ann Arbor, Mich.: University of Michigan Press, 1949).

84. Lado, Robert, *Language Teaching* (New York: McGraw-Hill Book Company, 1964).

85. ———, *Language Testing* (New York: Longmans, Green & Company, Inc., 1961).

86. ———, *Linguistics Across Cultures* (Ann Arbor, Mich.: University of Michigan Press, 1957).

87. Lambert, W. E., and S. Fillenbaum, "A Pilot Study of Aphasia Among Bilinguals," *Psycholinguistics,* Sol Saporta, ed. (New York: Holt, Rinehart & Winston, Inc., 1961).

88. Lane, Harlan, "Some Differences in First and Second Language Learning," *Language Learning,* XII (1962).

89. ——— and D. J. Moore, "Reconditioning a Consonant Discrimination in an Aphasic," *Journal of Speech and Hearing Disorders,* XXVII (August 1962)-

90. Langer, Susanne, *Philosophy in a New Key,* 2nd Ed. (New York: The New American Library of World Literature, Inc., 1961).

91. ———, "Speech and Its Communicative Function," *Quarterly Journal of Speech,* XLVI (1946).

92. Lee, Irving J., *Language Habits in Human Affairs* (New York: Harper & Row, Publishers, Inc., 1941).

93. Lentz, Lois B., and Dorothy Sherman, "Phonetic Elements and Perception of Nasality," *Journal of Speech and Hearing Research,* IV (December 1961).

94. Leutenegger, Ralph R., *The Sounds of American English* (Chicago: Scott, Foresman & Company, 1963).

95. Linton, Louise, "An Experimental Study of Speech Sound Discrimination" (unpublished Master's thesis), Leland Stanford Junior University, 1939.

96. Lotz, John, "On the Linguistic Structure of Speech," *Logos,* VI (April 1963).

97. Manser, Ruth B., *Speech Correction on the Contract Plan* (Englewood Cliffs, N.J.: Prentice-Hall, Inc., 1951).

98. Marland, Pauline, "Shadowing—A Contribution to the Treatment of Stammering," *Folia Phonetica,* IX (1957).

99. Meader, Clarence L., and John H. Muyskens, *Handbook of Biolinguistics,* 2nd Ed. (New York: Holt, Rinehart & Winston, Inc., 1962), Part I.

100. Menken, H. L., *The American Language* (New York: Alfred A. Knopf, Inc., 1936).

101. Mickleson, Leu R., "Form Classes: Structural Linguistics and Mechanical Translation," *For Roman Jakobson* (The Hague: Mouton and Company, 1956).

102. Milisen, Robert, "A Rational for Articulation Disorders," *Journal of Speech and Hearing Disorders,* Monograph Supplement, No. 4 (December 1954).

103. ———— *et al.,* "The Disorders of Articulation: A Systematic Clinical and Experimental Approach," *Journal of Speech and Hearing Disorders,* Monograph Supplement, No. 4 (December 1954).

104. Miller, George A., *Language and Communication* (New York: McGraw-Hill Book Company, 1951).

105. ————, "The Perception of Speech," *For Roman Jakobson,* Morris Halle, *et al.,* eds. (The Hague: Mouton and Company, 1956).

106. ————, and Patricia E. Nicely, "An Analysis of Perceptional Confusions Among Some English Consonants," *Psycholinguistics,* Sol Saporta, ed. (New York: Holt, Rinehart & Winston, Inc., 1961).

107. Moore, Paul G., Frazer D. White, and Hans von Leden, "Ultra High Speed Photography in Laryngeal Physiology," *Journal of Speech and Hearing Disorders,* XXVII (May 1962).

108. Moulton, William G., *The Sounds of English and German* (Chicago: The University of Chicago Press, 1962).

109. Mowrer, O. H., *Learning Theory and the Symbolic Processes* (New York: John Wiley, 1960).

110. Myklebust, Helmer, "The Differential Diagnosis of Deafness in Young Children," *Journal of Exceptional Children,* XVII (1951).

111. Nance, Lorna S., "Differential Diagnosis of Aphasia," *Journal of Speech and Hearing Disorders,* XI (September 1946).

112. Newman, Stanley S., "On the Stress System of English," *Word,* II (December 1946).

113. Nida, Eugene A., *Morphology: The Descriptive Analysis of Words,* 2nd Ed. (Ann Arbor, Mich.: University of Michigan Press, 1962).

114. Paratore, Angela, *English Dialogues for Foreign Students* (New York: Holt, Rinehart & Winston, Inc., 1957).

115. Pei, Mario, *One Language for the World* (New York: The Devin-Adair Company, 1958).

116. Peters, Robert W., "Dimension of Quality for the Vowel [æ]," *Journal of Speech and Hearing Research*, VI (September 1963).

117. Pfaff, Paul L., "The Moto-Kinesthetic Method Applied to Aphasics," *Journal of Speech and Hearing Disorders*, V (September 1940).

118. Portmann, Michel, and Claudine Portmann, *Clinical Audiometry* (Springfield, Ill.: Charles C. Thomas, Publisher, 1961).

119. Prator, Clifford H., Jr., *Manual of American English Pronunciation* (New York: Holt, Rinehart & Winston, Inc., 1957).

120. Rice, Donald B., and Robert Milisen, "The Influence of Increased Stimulation Upon the Production of Unfamiliar Sounds as a Function of Time," *Journal of Speech and Hearing Disorders*, Monograph Supplement, No. 4 (December 1959).

121. Rojas, Pauline, *American English Series*, Teachers Guide Books 1 and 2 (New York: D. C. Heath and Company, 1952).

122. Rosten, Leo, *The Return of Hyman Kaplan* (New York: Harper & Row, Publishers, Inc., 1959).

123. Ruesch, Jurgen, *Disturbed Communication* (New York: W. W. Norton & Company, Inc., 1957).

124. Sarett, Lew, W. T. Foster, and Alma J. Sarett, *Basic Principles of Speech*, 3rd Ed. (Boston: Houghton Mifflin Company, 1958).

125. *Sequential Tests of Educational Progress—Listening* (Los Angeles: Cooperative Test Division—Educational Testing Service, 1957).

126. Sheehan, Joseph G., "An Integration of Psychotherapy and Speech Therapy Through a Conflict Theory of Stuttering," *Journal of Speech and Hearing Disorders*, XIX (December 1954), 474-82.

127. Shen, Yoo, "Initial /r/ in American English and Mandarin Chinese and How to Teach It," *Language Learning*, II, No. 2 (April-June 1949).

128. Simon, Clarence T., "Complexity and Breakdown in Speech Situation," *Journal of Speech Disorders*, X (September 1945), 199-203.

129. Sinnott, Edmund W., *Plant Morphogenesis* (New York: McGraw-Hill Book Company, 1960).

130. Slager, William, ed., *English for Today*, The National Council of Teachers of English (New York: The McGraw-Hill Book Company, 1962).

131. Smith, Joseph, and James R. Linn, *Skill in Oral Reading* (New York: Harper & Row, Publishers, Inc., 1960).

132. Speech Committee of the Department of English, *Manual of Oral English Exercises*, English 105 (Rio Riedras, P.R.: Puerto Rico University, 1959-1960).

133. Stetson, R. H., *Motor Phonetics: A Study of Speech Movements in Action*, 2nd Ed. (Amsterdam: North-Holland Publishing Company for Oberlin College, 1951).

134. Stevens, Kenneth N., and Arthur S. House, "Perturbation of Vowel Articulations by Consonantal Context: An Acoustical Study," *Journal of Speech and Hearing Research*, VI (June 1963).

135. Templin, Mildred, "A Study of Sound Discrimination Ability of Elementary School Pupils," *Journal of Speech Disorders,* VIII (1943).

136. ———, and Frederic L. Darley, *The Templin-Darley Test of Articulation* (Iowa City, Iowa: Bureau of Educational Research and Service Extension Division, State University of Iowa, 1960).

137. Têng, Ssŭ-yü, *Conversational Chinese* (Chicago: University of Chicago Press, 1952).

138. Thomas, C. K., "Chinese Difficulties with English Pronunciations," *Journal of Speech and Hearing Disorders,* IV (September 1939).

139. Trager, George L., "Linguistics," *Encyclopedia Britannica* (1961), vol. 14, 163-171.

140. Travis, Lee Edward, *Handbook of Speech Pathology* (New York: Appleton-Century-Crofts, 1957).

141. ———, and Bessie Rasmus, "The Speech Sound Discrimination Ability of Cases with Functional Disorders of Articulation," *Quarterly Journal of Speech,* XVII (1931).

142. Tucker, Margaret F., "Listening Lessons in Connected Speech for Puerto Rican College Students for the Purpose of Improving Aural Comprehension in English," (unpublished Master's thesis), University of New Mexico, 1963.

143. Upton, Albert, *Design for Thinking* (Stanford, Calif.: Stanford University Press, 1961).

144. Van Riper, Charles, *Speech Correction: Principles and Methods,* 4th Ed. (Englewood Cliffs, N.J.: Prentice-Hall, Inc., 1963).

145. ——— and John V. Irwin, *Voice and Articulation* (Englewood Cliffs, N.J.: Prentice-Hall, Inc., 1958).

146. Vigotsky, L. S., "Thought and Speech," *Psychiatry,* II (1939).

147. Weinreich, Uriel, *Languages in Contact* (New York: The Linguistic Circle of New York, 1953).

148. Wendahl, Ronald W., and Jane Cole, "Identification of Stuttering During Relatively Fluent Speech," *Journal of Speech and Hearing Research,* IV (September 1961).

149. Whorf, Benjamin Lee, *Languages, Thought and Reality* (Boston, Mass.: Massachusetts Institute of Technology Press, with John Wiley & Sons, Inc., 1956).

150. ———, "The Relation of Habitual Thought and Behavior to Language," *Language, Culture and Personality,* Leslie Spier, *et al.,* eds., (Kenosha, Wis.: Sapir Memorial Publication Fund, 1941).

151. ———, "Science and Linguistics," *Readings in Applied Linguistics* (New York: Appleton-Century-Crofts, 1958).

152. Winitz, Harris, and Betty Bellrose, "Effects of Pretraining on Sound Discrimination Learning," *Journal of Speech and Hearing Research,* VI (June 1963).

153. Wise, Claude M., *Introduction to Phonetics* (Englewood Cliffs, N.J.: Prentice-Hall, Inc., 1958).

154. Yandell, Maurine Dunn, "Some Difficulties which Indian Children Encounter with Idioms in Reading" (unpublished Master's thesis), University of New Mexico, 1959.

155. Young, Edna Hill, and Sarah S. Hawk, *Moto-Kinesthetic Speech Training* (Stanford, Calif.: Stanford University Press, 1955).

index

A

Accent:
  expressive, 63-64
  in Spanish, 57-58
  stress in, 61
Adjustment to intonation patterns, 53
Adult approach to second language, 18
[æ] phoneme, 79-80
Allophone:
  of [æ], 80-81
  definition, xxxiv
  variants, 34
  of [ʊ], 82
Arabic, 85
  [æ] production, 81, 87-88
Arrangement, word, 11, 96
Articulation habits, xvii, 34, 37
Attitude:
  of clinician to foreign accent, 27
  toward foreign-language study, 23
Audiologist, xiv, xxv, 16
  language concept of, xxxiv
Auditory perception, 16-18
Aural-oral training method, xxxv, 9
  (*see also* Training methods)

B

Bantu language, 54
Bates, M., xxvii
Beals, R. L., and Hoijer, H., xxiii
Belgian Congo, 54
Bilabial fricative, 88

Bilingual, xv
  compound and coordinate, 14, 26
  true, 12-14, 18
Bilingual conditions in childhood, 24
Bronstein, A. J., 83
Burmese, 53
Burssens, A., 54

C

Carrell, J., and Tiffany, W., 45
Cases, xxix, 10, 63-64, 91
  French and diphthongs, 85-86
  intonation in Japanese, 51
  substitution for Schwa [ə], 77-78
  syllable stress, 57
  tone language, 53-54
  tone, Norwegian use of, 55
  unstressing, 78-79
Cherry, C., xviii
Chinese, 53-54, 58, 85, 92
  tone language, 53
  use of [æ], 79
Clinicians, 18, 39-40, 42, 55, 62, 96-97
  dialect investigation, 29
  preparation of materials, 52
  teaching stress, 61
  use of new grammar, 8
Cognates, 41-42
Colonizors, 22-23
Communication, xxiv, xxxiv
  definition, 30
  levels, xxix, 98
  process or concept of, xxi-xxiii, xxvii